S0-BOI-947

Science and Education
at the Crossroads

A VIEW FROM THE LABORATORY

Joseph William Still, M. D.

INTRODUCTION BY MALVINA LINDSAY

Public Affairs Press, Washington, D. C.

RICHMOND COLLEGE LIBRARY

TO MY PARENTS
AND MY WIFE HELEN

Copyright 1958, by Public Affairs Press
419 New Jersey Ave., S.E., Washington 3, D. C.
Printed in the United States of America
Library of Congress Catalog Card No. 58-10884

INTRODUCTION

Science and education have suddenly become everybody's business. Since the launching of the first Soviet space satellite, with its implications of an American lag in knowledge, citizens in all walks of life have been exercising their traditional freedom and spontaneity of speech to tell what is wrong at the fountainhead of our culture and achievement—our schools.

Nearly all of them stop there. They deplore, lament, accuse, but few come up with any ideas for constructive action. Many are content to call vaguely, though passionately, for a "reappraisal" or a "fundamental overhauling" of the educational system, or for a revival of good-old-days methods, or a copying of European ones.

The author of this book offers a refreshing and stimulating approach to the science-education controversy in his willingness to grasp the nettle of what-to-do. He follows his criticisms with concrete—and often controversial—proposals for having science play a more dynamic role both in education and in foreign policy.

The viewpoint of a working scientist on the needs of both American education and foreign relations has special pertinence now. Survival of the nation's cultural and political ideals depends increasingly on its progress in the sciences, both physical and social, basic and applied. Its part in the conquest of space and its status in the space age will be determined to a great extent by its scientific creativity.

Dr. Still brings to this discussion of our global and our outer space challenges the viewpoint of the classroom as well as the laboratory. He is experienced both in medical teaching and research. He has dealt widely with people, as a public health administrator and as an officer in the armed forces. He is no naive, sheltered scientist remote from life. His book testifies to the diversity of his experiences.

Some readers will disagree, perhaps violently, with some of his ideas. He has strong convictions and is forthright in stating them. Wading dauntlessly into one of the most controversial issues of the day, states rights, he makes a strong case for less "decentralization" in education, and for a greater role of the central government in this field. He will step on many professional toes in his attacks on what he calls "group-think" methods and "I.Q. fanatics" He has some currently unpopular things to say about what he regards as overemphasis on intelligence tests, on the cult of the gifted, and the segregation of the superior.

Among his proposals for increasing the nation's scientific creativity, two merit special consideration. One is for basic research investment in human beings rather than in projects; for life-long grants-in-aid that would give economic security and intellectual freedom to creative scientists. The other is for a pre-school program to encourage early the curiosity, natural interests, and possible scientific talents of all children, especially those from intellectually underprivileged homes.

His proposals for having scientists participate more directly in government at policy making levels may cause many a politician to shudder, and are not likely to find prompt fulfillment. But he has called attention in an arresting manner to the way in which a people, while calling on scientists to be their saviors, yet deny them opportunity to relate their knowledge in a meaningful way to problems of government and foreign policy. Moreover, the activities of politics increasingly affect the work of scientists. Streams of influence flow both ways.

This book is primarily concerned with what education and science can do to further world peace, and the author does not lack for specific proposals on foreign policy. At a time when biological science has, unfortunately, been neglected in government science programs, Dr. Still presents a bold plan for using it as a "positive tool of diplomacy." A program of biological aid to underdeveloped nations, aimed at ending ignorance, hunger, disease, poverty, over-population, is, he maintains, the most realistic road to peace.

Some of these proposals may seem Utopian now, but, as the author points out, the feasibility of several that he has pioneered, has already been demonstrated by their espousal by "practical" men. In others he has blazed trails of thought into which action may gradually venture.

Whether readers of this book question, doubt, applaud or denounce, they are not likely to read it with minds unstirred. They will find they have received a strong prod "from the laboratory" to use their own minds in more informed and energetic thought as to how this nation can meet the pressing and mounting demands on its mental resources.

MALVINA LINDSAY

Washington, D. C.

PREFACE

In writing this book I have attempted a general analysis of our present crisis in science and education.

Part I discusses the short-range problems of science and education. Our weaknesses in these areas can, if we choose, be corrected in the relatively near future—in a few years at the most. Part II considers the long-range problem of how we can best use our scientific and industrial strength and prestige to improve the prospect of achieving a lasting world peace. This is at least a problem of decades.

My professional experience has brought me into direct contact with many aspects of the problems of which I am writing. During World War II, I spent two years in North Africa and Italy in the Mediterranean Theater of Operations Surgeon's Office. I witnessed and studied the staggering poverty and ignorance and disease in which the North African Arabs exist. As the Assistant to Colonel William S. Stone, the wise medical soldier who foresaw the U.S. military need to discover a good insecticide, I was privileged to witness the introduction of D.D.T., first to stop the Naples typhus epidemic and then as an anti-malaria weapon. These wartime experiences provided the fundamental viewpoint underlying Part II of this book. They taught me, as nothing else could, the importance of science in connection with military and foreign affairs.

An American who witnesses the awful toll that poverty and ignorance are exacting in the underdeveloped areas of the world is bound to realize that the basic cause of these terrible conditions is not a lack of machines or a lack of sanitation, but a lack of education. It also becomes clear that it is hopeless to direct idealistic propaganda slogans at ignorant, poverty-stricken, hungry people. It is foolish to expect them to give much thought to anything other than the satisfaction of their immediate physical needs.

Having concluded that education is the basic tool for achieving an end to poverty and disease, and for achieving a peaceful world, I then realized that our first step must be to understand the world in which we live. Unless most Americans see that there is a practical, common-sense relationship between their own well-being and that of the rest of the world, it is absurd to expect them willingly to pay taxes to support foreign aid. This book attempts to show how science provides the key to understanding our problems and our relationships to the rest of the world.

Because the greatest contributions of science have been in the direction of extending life rather than in creating weapons of death, I cannot help but feel that our country should be able to use biological science as a positive tool of diplomacy. There is something wrong with policies which seem to place our first line of defense on the negative nuclear weapons of death.

Since the war I have been working in basic research and medical school teaching. Like many of my fellow scientists, I have been disturbed by the fact that science has more and more come to be—or seemed to be—synonymous with weapons, destruction, and death. Though there are legitimate reasons for using science for military purposes, it should by now be apparent that no modern government can afford to neglect biology for very long. After all, governments are composed of biological animals. If governments put so much of their energy into "defending" themselves from potential future threats that they have no energy to devote to improving human existence here and now, they run a grave risk of disintegration. Nations, like people, are constantly in a dynamic, changing state. If they do not grow and expand and progress, they tend to stagnate, shrivel and recede.

Part I deals with the more obvious and immediate and generally recognized specific problems of improving our scientific and educational organization. During the post-war years, I have had first-hand experience with several aspects of these problems. In addition to the reason stated above, I write about these topics for two other reasons: (1) Because we have not yet had a general discussion of these matters by a working scientist, and (2) because I believe that to solve our science and education problems, we must have more planning and financing and considerably more leadership at the national level than we now have.

With the exception of Rear Admiral H. G. Rickover, almost everyone who has been heard on these matters has continued to accept the present complete decentralization of education as sacrosanct and immutable. Because I have assumed that a certain amount of national planning and a large amount of national leadership are desirable in these areas, I have arrived at conclusions and solutions which are different from most that have been offered us so far.

In Part II I have outlined what I believe is a feasible way to direct the cold war into useful biological competition. Science and education are the basic tools recommended for this task.

Fortunately, there is no reason to doubt that this country has the vitality to reorient itself and get back to the role which won it the love and admiration of the world—as the nation which produced the highest standard of living ever achieved for millions of people and which has always been ready to give generous aid to other peoples struggling to free themselves from oppression, poverty, ignorance or disease.

Whether I have succeeded in clarifying the "big picture", only time can tell. I have received encouragement in this regard from the fact that some of my suggestions, which seemed somewhat impractical when first voiced to some of my friends only a few months ago, have already been advocated by some very practical Americans. I am thinking, for example, of the idea that scientists from business, professions and Government participate in high school instruction—a proposal which General David Sarnoff has publicly espoused. I also have in mind the proposal made recently by Senator A. S. (Mike) Monroney for the establishmen of a World "Second Mortgage" Bank; and the related suggestion of Benjamin A. Javits, lawyer-economist, who proposed the formation of a World Development Corporation to channel private capital into foreign economic development.

*   *   *   *

Writing a book such as this causes one to recall his many intellectual debts, and to wish he could acknowledge every one of them. Since this is impossible, I must confine myself to expressing my appreciation to those who have made more or less direct contributions to this book. Many of these debts are noted in the text, but a few individuals, though not directly quoted, have had a significant relationship to the ideas expressed here. These are:

Mr. Jaroslav Nemec, Librarian of the Washington office of the American Medical Association, who furnished data on physicians, dentists and engineers in Congress.

Mr. C. L. Zakhartchenko, consultant on guided missiles and space travel, who provided many stimulating observations concerning present-day research problems.

Dr. Archibald T. MacPherson, Associate Director, National Bureau of Standards, who provided me with information concerning the development of interest in Science Clubs, an activity to which he has contributed greatly.

Dr. Nancy Bayley, psychologist of the National Institutes of Health, for criticism of Chapter V.

Many teachers, and especially Dr. Douglas Noble of the Washington School of Psychiatry from whom I learned a great deal concerning modern views of psychiatry.

Dr. Errett C. Albritton, who introduced me to the elements of basic research in physiology, and who with his successor, Dr. Chester E. Leese, created in their department at The George Washington University Medical School a climate of research freedom which encouraged neophyte investigators to try their own wings.

Drs. George Stoddard, H.M. Skeels and co-workers who made the basic studies of child psychology (known as the "Iowa Studies") which demonstrated the great changeability of the I.Q.—work which greatly influenced Chapter V.

Dr. Curt Richter, whose article "Free Research versus Design Research" (*Science*, July 24, 1953) provided several of the basic ideas of Chapter IX.

Dr. Stella Deignan of Biosciences Information Exchange and Dr. Karl Heumann of Biochemical Abstracts, who supplied me with a great deal of information concerning the problems of scientific communication discussed in chapter X.

Mr. Robert C. Cook and Mr. Hugh C. Davis of the Population Reference Bureau, who provided much useful information concerning the population explosion now in progress. Kingsley Davis' article "The Unpredicted Pattern of Population Change," which appeared in the *Annals of the American Academy of Political and Social Science* was also of great value in this connection.

Dr. Louis L. Williams of the Pan American Sanitary Bureau, who provided much of the information concerning the effects of D.D.T. in underdeveloped areas.

Drs. Erwin Steinman and Frank D. Allan of The George Washington Medical School, whose thoughtful criticisms have been of real value to me.

My wife and Hugh Morrow, who contributed greatly to improvement of the readability of the book.

Mrs. Doris Soares, Mrs. Selma Klein and Miss Bonnie Burton, who patiently translated my scribbled, messy drafts into clear, neat type.

All responsibility for errors of fact or interpretation are of course my own.

JOSEPH WILLIAM STILL

Washington, D. C.

CONTENTS

ABOUT THE AUTHOR

Joseph William Still, M.D., is a medical scientist with broad experience in his field as researcher, teacher, practitioner, administrator and author, but he is primarily a laboratory scientist. His recent research on the cause of aging and on blood factors related to strokes and heart disease, and his contributions to space medicine, have atrracted wide attention in scientific circles.

As a Lieutenant Colonel in the Army Medical Corps during World War II, assigned to the Mediterranean Theatre of Operations, Dr. Still observed at first hand the dramatic victory of American medical science over malaria and typhus in Italy. Since the war, as a member of the faculty of the George Washington University School of Medicine in Washington, D. C., he has not only taught budding young scientists and future physicians, but has fostered special projects designed to interest high school students in science careers. The latter activity began several years before the advent of Sputnik I made such recruitment a national preoccupation. He is the author of numerous scientific, educational and medical articles. In addition he also writes for general non-professional publications.

Dr. Still received his M.D. degree from the University of Nebraska in 1936, and the Johns Hopkins University awarded him the degree of Master of Public Health in 1941. He has pursued additional studies at the Washington School of Psychiatry and the George Washington University in the fields of psychiatry, physiology, biochemistry, pathology and neurology.

PART I

THE SHORT-RANGE VIEW

In the chapters of Part I all major aspects of the science-education crisis are considered. The general topics covered are the organization and administration of science, both in and out of government; motivation and encouragement of students; improvement of teaching and expansion of research; financial and other support for teachers and scientists; and communication between scientists and between science and the general public. With respect to each topic, three major questions are considered:

1. What is wrong?
2. How did we go wrong?
3. What must we do to correct our weaknesses?

Because the territory covered in these chapters is so large, it is necessary that the "picture" be painted with a "broad brush". It is believed that such a presentationi showing all major aspects and their inter-relations as part of a whole problem, will be of real value. There have been so many different criticisms and suggestions since Sputnik I, that the average non-scientist has probably been led to believe that there are even more differences between scientists and educators than there really are. It is intended that these chapters will provide a skeleton framework for relating fragmentary data and comments to the general picture; a picture which is likely to remain before us for some time.

CHAPTER I

THE REALITIES OF THE SPACE AGE

American scientists responded to Sputnik I by generously congratulating the Soviet scientists on their success. Their good sportsmanship was not emulated by our politicians, caught with their Vanguard down. While "beep-beep-beep" messages were bringing Sputnik's scientific data to earth, more subtle messages—"too little, too late; too little, too late"—were also reaching us.

Since the Sputniks began orbiting, the eyes of the public have been opened. The American people are becoming increasingly aware of facts about our science and education which have been too long ignored. For several years, there have been many who saw, and reported on, weaknesses in our science and education. But their messages were drowned in the din of automobiles and appliances rolling off the lines—a din supposedly proving that we had achieved The Best of All Possible Worlds.

We are now awakening to the realities. Our pride has been hurt. We have been beaten in a field in which almost all our political leaders, and even many of our scientific leaders, have said we had a clear and unbeatable advantage. It is obvious that they could neither see, interpret, nor face the facts. The evidence was there and it should have been a warning to those able and willing to see and understand. Some of our leaders still are not facing the facts. In many instances, to do so would require them to admit that they had been the victims of their own delusions and their own propaganda. This is psychologically too painful an admission to make.

Although facts demonstrate that we are not properly organized to compete efficiently with Soviet science, many are telling us that all we need are a few "crash" programs. Such programs would do essentially the same things we have been doing for the past twelve years. During those years, the Soviets, beginning almost from scratch, overtook and passed American science in several important areas in which we originally had a tremendous head start.

After ridiculing Soviet science for so many years, it is hard for us to admit that we have been guilty of false pride. But, if we are to re-establish a sound basis for justifiable pride in the accomplishments which have made us a great nation, we must make this admission as a starting point. Then we must take a cold, hard look at our whole scientific organization and our entire educational system.

There is evidence that important reforms, some of them radical, are essential at almost every level of our educational system *if we hope to maintain a leading position* in the realm of science and technology. It is no longer realistic to think that we can have absolute supremacy in these fields. The mere restoration of our educational standards to levels which will keep us among the world's science leaders will necessitate stepping on some toes, some of them pretty important and tender ones.

This book is my effort as a working scientist to appraise our scientific and educational organization as I would appraise a research problem. I hope thereby to help the American people arrive at a correct diagnosis of a problem which is new and puzzling to all of us. In the field of medicine, I have often seen the disastrous results of a physician's confusing symptoms with causes. In appraising our national situation, we are in danger from too much concern with symptoms and too little with causes.

The fundamental argument of this book is that what the American people need to ask themselves is not, "How can we catch up with Russia in the satellite and rocket fields?" Instead, we need to re-examine our whole attitude toward science and education and ask such questions as these:

1.   Are our national attitudes toward science and education sound?

2.   Is our present educational philosophy adequate to meet today's challenges?

3.   Since so many of us move from state to state and from city to city (about 27% of all high school graduates, 25 to 34 years old, have been interstate migrants at least once), can we run a sensible educational system without establishing an overall national educational program and setting some kind of nation-wide educational standards?

4.   Would a nationally-planned, locally-implemented, program necessarily be undemocratic or un-American?

5.   Must a "free" society leave the individual youngster "free" to choose not to educate himself or a community free to neglect the education of its children?

6.   What do we expect from science? Can science fulfill these expectations? Is American science properly organized to fulfill them?

7.   Is money all that is needed to gain the support of scientists?

8. What facilities and support must science have to accomplish the goals we settle on?

9. How can scientists and the public be motivated to work for these goals?

10. Can science flourish if it is used principally as a weapon of death?

None of these questions has been adequately considered in developing the various "crash" programs suggested so far. One of the most remarkable features of the Space Age, so far as Americans are concerned, has been the speed with which our officials have been able to explain our defeat. The great speed with which they have suggested remedies has been equally remarkable. We have been told, in effect, that all we need do to get ahead of the Russians is to adopt a few gimmicks, appropriate more money, stop the "foolish" economy drive, "pool" all the scientific brains of the NATO countries, create more scholarships for "gifted" students, and do some touching up in our economy here and there.

Our Secretary of Health, Education and Welfare, Marion B. Folsom, has placed himself on public record as "opposed to any fundamental change in the American educational system, despite deep concern over the dramatic advances of Soviet technical education." This statement provides a good point at which to start the analysis of our educational difficulties. Unhappily, what Mr. Folsom says represents the dominant and prevailing view today. No scientist deserving of the name would ever approach a scientific problem in this negative fashion. He would first analyze the problem while trying consciously to avoid any preconceived thoughts concerning final solutions. Certainly he would not say, "I will solve the problem only if I can do so without making any fundamental changes."

Important problems almost always involve fundamentals. Since fundamentals sometimes grow outmoded, I believe we have no choice but to examine the very roots of our educational system. In fact, in a dynamic age such as we live in, we must continuously maintain a review of many aspects of our national life. Had we been doing this, the task of alerting us to the weaknesses in our educational system would not have been left to the Sputniks.

The aim of American education, in Folsom's opinion, must continue to be the development of "broadly-educated men who have the intellectual ability and the moral conviction to make those difficult and unpopular decisions that determine the course of mankind's advance. These qualities require not only a grasp of science but also of the humanities." This is a desirable goal, but has our present educational program been achieving it? We know our educational system has not been emphasizing science. For several years before Sputnik, we had a spate of books and articles showing that our present educational system was *failing* to produce college students who could read and write as well as their parents did. In our present situation, we must not ignore that evidence. Our educational program needs to be overhauled so it will produce both scientists and humanists who are "broadly educated." No humanist can claim he is "broadly educated" if he does not know the fundamentals of physics, chemistry and biology. There is no contradiction between being "broadly educated" and being scientifically educated. Science is not opposed to humanistic values. What is inhuman about studying nature? Science is a humanistic endeavor.

The chapters which follow show that if we are to maintain a position of essential equality vis-a-vis the Soviet and other rapidly-progressing economies all over the world, we must:

1. Greatly expand and improve our present educational facilities. We must modernize *all* our schools so that *all* our children are educated to perform useful roles in our modern technological society. They must be educated *both* in science and in the humanities.

2. Stop accepting the present teacher shortages as inevitable and find ways to get and keep enough good teachers to maintain the highest educational standards. We cannot accept less. To do this, of course, we must restore the prestige of our teachers both with adults and with children.

3. Establish national educational standards and programs so that a child may move from Florida or Maine to Minnesota or California or vice versa without encountering new and confusing standards at every move. Though present disruptions are difficult to evaluate in toto, no one can doubt they are very important to the individual children involved.

4. Greatly increase the time our children spend in schools, end the creed of permissiveness, and insist that children be educated in depth for the kind of society in which they must live.

5. Provide teachers and scientists with the solid capitalist rewards of pay and prestige on a scale comparable to those provided by the "anti-capitalist" Soviets. Stop believing that we can staff our school system with "dedicated teachers" who are willing to work mainly for the enjoyment of teaching and to ignore the low pay and prestige of teachers today. These notions spring from a "something for

nothing" idea that never has worked for long any place. If scientists are valuable, then the teaching necessary to produce them is equally valuable, and we must pay for it in accordance with its value.

6. Dispel the nonsensical doctrine that only the "gifted" can be scientists and stop the I. Q. fanatics with their pigeon-hole, punch-card techniques from completely undermining the morale of our schools with their oversimplified theories of intelligence. We must confine the I. Q. concept to the psychological research and diagnostic role in which it can be useful. It is not a tool suited for general public use, no more so than the tools of medicine and surgery.

The present organization of Soviet science, technology and educa-tion is actually superior to ours in many ways. The Russians have created enticing rewards for those who enter science. As a result a far larger percentage of their children than ours are studying dili-gently to become scientists. They are being taught more science *and more humanities* in fewer years than ours are. They have far more teachers in relation to the number of students than we have. Their methods of distributing scientific information to their scientists are so superier to ours as to make our system look archaic.

Khrushchev claims that these and other superiorities are due to an inherent advantage deriving from their Socialist economic organi-zation. This claim is not easy to disprove. In 1945, the U.S.S.R. was a half-devasted, war-weary, backward nation. The Russians' in-dustrial power had been growing over the years, but to a large extent their factories were not much more than slavish copies of earlier Amer-ican and European plants. In 1945 they certainly had no outstanding superiority over us *in any area* of science or technology. Yet in twelve years they achieved first place in rocket design and manu-facture and they are at least in second and possibly in first place in several other important areas—such as the production of jet planes, the development of atomic power, and the design of submarines and helicopters.

Americans believe that free enterprise can out-produce socialist organization. The test is now on. If vested interests prevent our making many needed reforms in this country, we shall not only fall further behind the Soviets, but soon we may find ourselves over-taken and surpassed by still other and more dynamic nations as well. In that case, free-enterprise private capitalism would hardly appear an attractive pattern for backward countries to emulate.

At the time the Soviets exploded their first atom bomb, we were told this was made possible only because the Rosenbergs and Dr.

Fuchs had passed them "the secret." We countered their A-bomb with our great secrecy program. Their H-bomb success was passed off as a piece of experimental good luck or accident. Their recent successes with jet planes and long-range rockets began to undermine these theories. The successful launching of the artificial satellites utterly shattered such explanations.

We must face the blunt truth that, as of this moment, Soviet science appears to be better than ours. In this fast-moving world, it does not take long to fall into the ruck. German science and medicine, clearly at the top or near the top in almost every phase during the 1910-1920 period, fell to a third-rate world position by 1940 under the mismanagement and disorganizing influence of Naziism. We cannot afford the mistake of thinking it can't happen here. If we choose, we can meet the Soviet challenge without adopting totalitarian principles and without wrecking our national budget.

The unfortunate state of our science mechanism does not imply that our scientists are second-rate. They definitely are not. In fact, a considerable part of our difficulty arises from the fact that we seldom recognize an outstanding American until he receives some prize or recognition in Europe.

Our scientific organization, as compared with the Soviets, is so cumbersome and so uncoordinated that it scarcely merits the name. The basic characteristic of an organization is that it possess established, well-functioning communication channels and accepted principles for their use, that it be able to act and react with decent speed and precision. In these terms, our science is comparable to the Portugese Man-Of-War, an "organism" made up of millions of cells which exist as a formidable colony when "organized." But under some circumstances, the millions of cells may suddenly part company, each going its merry way. The whole system is brought to a sudden end. The "organism" is constantly subject to complete chaos and possesses no mechanisms to prevent it. Thus cellular "freedom" is carried to the absurd point which permits complete dissolution.

At this point, some may think I am about to suggest that American science be converted into a scientific beehive. This will not be my suggestion—quite the contrary. However, we have made such a fetish of individualism that we often border on anarchy. This has not brought American scientists real freedom. In fact they have had too little. There is need for certain kinds of discipline among scientists if we are to reorganize so we can compete with the Soviets.

But the disciplinary steps that are necessary are of the largely self-imposed kind that accompany mature responsibility. They are not those of a police state. The freedom of individual scientists will be enhanced, not hampered, by their organizing themselves more effectively. Fortunately, there are growing signs that more and more scientists are coming to this realization.

Chapter II

SCIENCE REPRESENTATION IN GOVERNMENT

"Do it yourself" has a long and honorable history in science. Until about 100 years ago, there were almost no full-time professional scientists—only wealthy hobbyists or part-time devotees. Many of these were very capable, nonetheless. Ben Franklin's kite experiment, in which he showed that lightning is due to an electrical discharge, is a perfect illustration.

Gradually, with industrial growth and with the accumulation of wealth, a few men began to make science a full-time pursuit. But aside from the few who were supported by patrons, only the well-to-do could afford a way of life that brought no income. Naturally, early science was almost exclusively of the basic type. Applied science did not exist as a form of business or as a way of earning a living. In such circumstances anyone who was interested in scientific matters had to perform his own experiments—as quite a few did. It was essentially an intellectual tool with which one might investigate interesting problems. The who-done-it and the crossword puzzle had not been invented, and basic science may have been something of a diversion as well as an occasional occupational necessity for teachers, druggists, farmers, physicians, engineers, and others. This part-time amateur status was possible because science was still in a technically crude state in which most of the important questions could be investigated with very crude instruments.

The body of accumulated knowledge was also so relatively small that it was not too difficult for a well-educated person to have a good basic understanding of all areas of science. The techniques of science were so simple that it was even possible to be technically proficient in most branches of science.

Specialism and technology had hardly begun. Consequently a small number of men, without using special consultants, could operate a large business, an army or a government. They could establish policies and plan operations without fear of overlooking some obscure technicality which might disrupt a whole elaborate scheme. Any small group of well-educated men could be counted on to know most of the important facts needed to solve almost any question.

Because of the relative technical simplicity of our early economy and of early American life in general, the problems of government were relatively simple as well. Service in the Congress was a part-time task; much of it still is in most of our state legislatures. For this reason, many teachers, physicians and farmers were members of the early Congresses. They brought a broad cross-section of community life into the national legislative halls and with them came a considerable leaven of science, relatively undeveloped though it was. Science was equally well represented in other branches of government and in other aspects of community life.

Proof that science was far better represented in those early days of our nation is also to be found in the fact that 6 of the 56 men who signed the Declaration of Independence were physicians. In contrast, there were only 6 physicians and dentists combined among the 528 men in the 85th Congress. There also were only 7 engineers in the 85th Congress, making a total of 13 applied scientists. This is less than 3% of the total.

As legislation gradually became more time-consuming and finally became a full-time, year-'round job, practicing scientists, physicians, engineers and teachers have been less and less represented in Congress. Obviously, even one term in Congress would leave a scientist, physician, or engineer out of touch with his special field and so tend to undermine his professional competence. This is why lawyers and business men have so dominated Congress in recent years.

Science as a full-time occupation did not begin on any important scale till the late nineteenth century. Louis Pasteur in France and Thomas Edison in the United States were among the earliest full-time scientists who did not have independent income. They were among the pioneers who showed that basic science could be applied to make wealth. Thus scientific and technical specialism as a profession is a development largely of this century.

With the development of specialization, science (especially in this country) has tended to be looked on largely as a technique. Our overemphasis on technology was made possible by the abundant pool of "free" basic information available to our industries without cost. This information was "free" because Europe over the preceding two or three centuries had supported most of those who had made the basic discoveries on which our technology rested. This situation has had much to do with the fact that, until now, government and industry have been more interested in promoting inventions than in fostering fundamental ideas and research. Basic science ideas, facts and theories about nature, could not be patented. Since no price tag could be placed on them, their value was not appreciated.

The United States was busy expanding and growing. Massive immigration and abundant resources provided us a vast and ever-growing home market. So many "free" ideas were available; why should any one spend money and effort to get more of them? All that was necessary was to learn how to exploit the "free" ones already available and millions could be made.

Now we have suddenly realized that in our over-specialization, we have allowed ourselves to become isolated from an understanding of the broad social implications of science, and from a full appreciation of basic science. Unfortunately many have been called scientists who have shared these public attitudes. There are too many called scientists who are only high-grade technicians with no real comprehension of the deeper values of science. This is, in part at least, the reason many people feel that science and scientists are at odds with the humanists—if not actually anti-humanist.

The contention of some "scientists" that the social implications of science are none of their business encourages the rather general public belief that scientists are unfeeling robots. Needless to say, certain politicians have encouraged this attitude. Many Americans believe that *all* scientists are mere technicians who, because of their emphasis on science, are and must be uncultured and ignorant of everything going on outside their laboratories. As I have just said, this is no doubt true of some "scientists," but it certainly is not true of many of our best ones—men such as Vannevar Bush, Norbert Weiner, Rene Dubos, Irvine Page and Linus Pauling, to name only a few. That we do not have more truly broad-gauged scientists, and fewer technicians who are mislabeled "scientists," is not the fault of science per se, but of faulty educational values.

Our national economic and social development has been such that basic science is today hardly represented in the higher echelons of business, labor and government. Basic scientists merely serve as technical consultants who answer questions *when they are asked*. They are almost completely excluded from asking questions in policy-making roles for they are seldom present at the discussions. The disclosure that Mrs. Oveta Culp Hobby, former Secretary of Health, Education and Welfare, set a deadline of seventy-five minutes on the committee trying to decide whether or not to release Salk vaccine clearly displays the situation of which I speak. It also demonstrates that she had little understanding of the nature of scientific decisions.

By and large, non-scientists can recognize a scientific "trouble spot" only when it has become a fairly obvious one. Because science is so poorly represented at the planning and policy levels of present day government and business, the science aspects of many matters are too often late in being recognized. Problems which modern science could prevent are too often allowed to grow to dimensions which make them far more difficult to correct or remove than would have been true had they been recognized and corrective action started earlier. Such lapses would happen much less often if scientists were *at* the conference tables continuously, instead of merely being used as consultants when called like glorified bellhops.

Modern science is often subtle. These subtleties are often overlooked under present circumstances. There could be no clearer proof of our ignorance of the subtleties of science than the mishandling of the firing of the first Vanguard satellite. If scientists had really been in complete control of this project, as they should have been, there would not have been the psychologically stupid publicity build-up. In this case the experiment was made a tool of the publicity bureaus. This arrangement placed those in charge of the satellite launching under terrible pressures which have no place in a scientific laboratory. It is unfortunate that the scientists did not refuse to operate under these circumstances. Their failure to insist that the experiment take priority over the publicity has embarrassed themselves, our science and our government.

When President Eisenhower held his first large-scale conference to consider the strategic implications of Sputnik, not a single working scientist was present among the thirty-plus men in attendance. This clearly indicated the measure of science's role at that time. President Eisenhower's subsequent appointment of Dr. James Killian, to the White House staff pointed up the inadequate representation of science in the upper levels of government. Whether this position carries sufficient authority and prestige to adequately represent science in the formulation of high policy remains to be demonstrated.

To show the unfortunate effect of this failure of science to be better represented in planning national policy, let us consider the following situation: Many of our biological scientists have played leading roles in perfecting marvelous new tools of life. D.D.T., penicillin and polio vaccine are only the best known; there are numerous other human, animal and plant disease-control methods which they have perfected. Yet when high policy is being formed in government these tools are too often overlooked. The physical sciences are at least represented by men with engineering backgrounds, but there is no one present in the Cabinet with first hand knowledge of biological science. At the time Sputnik I was launched there was not a single science attache in the State Department. I suspect that many of the "hard-headed" business men in government may think of malaria control as international social welfare programs. Probably the basic reason the government has not "sold" Foreign Aid more effectively to the American people is that there is no one present at these top meetings to "sell" these top officials themselves on these programs. Such programs come up from below. In such circumstances, programs often are poorly presented and defended and so get off to bad starts even when carried out. The satellite program which was the basis of interservice dispute for months seems to offer many illustrations of this point.

In the numerous disputes over the control of atomic energy and radiation hazards over the past ten years, many of the final decisions were rendered against a large body, often an apparent majority, of scientific opinion. Since government-employed physicists design bombs and guided missiles, they are of course *consulted,* often privately, by government policymakers dealing with these matters. But other scientists, especially those outside of government, have usually had to address any dissenting opinions to the public press. Of course, the opinion of science should not settle every issue. But science is too important today to have only a secondary role.

Only a few weeks before Sputnik, Secretary of Defense Charles E. Wilson consolidated research and development in the Defense Department, placing basic research activities under a development engineer. His ideas about the value of basic research were made very clear at that time when he said that someone other than the military should carry on fundamental research "as to what makes the grass green". One can even suspect from this remark that Mr. Wilson had never heard of the flow of solar energy to green grass to gasoline to automobile power.

The reports of the Fairless and Rockefeller committees, both containing a predominance of businessmen, also illustrate the way other businessmen tend to overemphasize "hardware" technology and underestimate "green grass". Up to a point, this is certainly understandable, and it is not cited in criticism of these men as individuals. In the specialized world in which we live, people tend to know most about the fields in which they specialize. Businessmen specialize in "hardware" and basic scientists specialize in "green grass". Perhaps some scientists tend to be over-enthusiastic about "green grass" and its potentials, though in the shadow of the satellites it is hard to accept such a judgement. The point is that such committees usually contain few if any working scientists. Not only business, but *every* worthwhile and important occupation and activity in our society should influence national policy if we hope to have well-balanced government. They must *all* be adequately represented at the policy-making levels of government. Basic science and even technical science and education are not so represented today and the nation is the poorer for it.

A related question is this: Why is it that physicists and electronic engineers working in weapons development (applied Necrology) can command salaries considerably higher than biological scientists working on research whose goal it is to extend man's life or make life healthier and happier? Of course, the Administration has ballyhooed the Peaceful Atom, and its potential is indeed great. There can be no doubt that President Eisenhower strongly believes in Atoms for Peace. But despite the ballyhoo, the first post-Sputnik increase in salaries for government scientists specifically excluded biological scientists. Our biologists have made many really stunning discoveries. But the public, including our political leaders, is too largely unaware of them. It has often been demonstrated in the area of foreign aid that our government does not know how to use them with full effectiveness.

What explains this lack of knowledge and understanding of our own science? Why have our leaders failed to note how poorly science, biological as well as physical, is represented in the upper levels of government? Why have there been no efforts to create prestige positions in the Cabinet and Congress to be held by scientific leaders? Probably all the other questions of this book can be subsummed under these two. Briefly, the answer is that the leaders of this country have not valued science and education to the degree that European nations have because we have obtained too much basic science "free". "Free" things seldom are valued correctly. But European nations in which science has had a complete development know the costs and value of the product. And in those countries and especially in the U.S.S.R., science has played an important policy-making role.

To correct our present deficiency, the President should appoint one or more Secretaries of Science without portfolio. Probably there should be at least two, one representing biological and one representing physical science. The two fields of science are sufficiently distinct to justify separate Secretaries. To some people this may seem a radical proposal. But when we consider the importance of science now and its undoubtedly increasing future importance, is such a suggestion really radical?

To provide also adequate science representation in Congress, I suggest the establishment of Delegate Senators and Representatives, essentially as has been advocated for ex-Presidents. Such scientists-Congressmen should have the power to introduce legislation and enjoy full floor and perhaps limited committee privileges. They probably should not even vote on committees, certainly not on the legislation before Congress. These posts might be held by the presidents of major scientific organizations, but it would probably be better still if scientific bodies elected specific representatives to them. Such jobs might not require full-time, year-'round attendance, since these Delegate Congressmen would not vote. Only experience could determine that point. If it turns out that these people must spend a great deal of time in Washington, suitable research facilities could be developed to enable them to maintain contact with their scientific work while resident in the capital. Thus, working scientists could hold these jobs without getting seriously out of contact with their professional work.

The science crisis we now are in is in large degree an educational crisis which has resulted from our following the concept of decentralized control and support of education too far. As will be evident at many points in this book, we must have a national education "headquarters" to represent the public's and especially our childrens' interest, and to serve as a forum in which to debate the educational problems we face. To accomplish this, I propose that we establish a National Education Council. The Council would perform in the educational realm a role somewhat analogous to that performed in the economic realm by the Council of Economic Advisors or the Federal Reserve Board. The members of the Council should serve on a full-time life-tenure basis. They should be distinguished citizens and as a group should be broadly representative of all aspects of our national life. The Council would not administer anything except itself.

The specific responsibilities of the Council would be: 1. To constantly study and report on our total educational system. 2. To make continuing publicly reported estimates of the future educational needs of our country. 3. To publicly recommend, in broad terms, the kind of curriculum and standards our schools must follow to prepare youngsters for the estimated future.

Any one who has anything to do with planning curricula or educational standards, should be cognizant of the future for which he is planning. Obviously most school boards and individuals at present have very limited facilities for making such studies. Of course they also have essentially *no* way of discussing their different estimates with each other in order to effect coordination. So we have, in theory at least, 48 or more different curricula or standards. In a society in which parents (and hence children) are as mobile as ours are, can this lead to anything but intellectual confusion and educational inefficiency for those children who must transfer from one school district to another one?

Sixty years ago our medical education was in a similar crisis, the result of extreme decentralization. In 1900 there were 160 medical schools, mostly very inadequate ones. The medical profession, through the American Medical Association, took charge of reforming the situation. A single national minimum standard of medical education and a "suggestive" curriculum was established. Schools were then inspected annually and graded A, B or C. The grades were published. At first there were schools in all three grades, but now all of our 82 schools have achieved grade A status. In the course of the reform, American medical practice and education have moved from a poor second rate position to one at or near the top relative to the rest of the nations of the world. We should be able to learn a great deal from a study of that experience to help us in this present situation. It is probably not necessary that such a Council have any police power. If it has sufficient prestige and establishes sensible standards its recommendations will carry great weight.

Perhaps the basic reason science is so poorly represented in government is due to our persistence in the notion that educational matters—all educational matters—are no affair of our federal government. We still act as though science was *only* (sic) an educational matter when in fact science and the educational system to maintain it are the very cement that makes our national way of life possible.

We have made a fetish of the claim that educational policy must be decided in thousands of local school boards. When mass education was 3-R education for 3-R rural living this worked very well. But the U.S. has grown from a nation which in 1850 was 85% rural to one which in 1950 was 65% urbanized. Actually this understates the case for many of the 35% living in rural areas actually work full- or part-time in industrial jobs. We are now a nation whose people are almost as mobile as nomads. Mobile people in an industrial society need high levels of technical education if they are to be economically useful. Can anyone doubt that the children of mobile parents will be educationally harmed if every parental move brings upsetting changes in curriculum, educational standards, teaching methods and goals, and so on for the child. How can such educational disruption be averted, except by our at least developing some national mechanism for establishing a single curriculum and a single set of educational standards for the whole nation.

Admiral H. G. Rickover, who built the world's first atom-powered submarine, has said this on the subject:

"The greatest single obstacle to a renovation of our education comes from the fact that control, financing and direction of education is, in the U.S., in the hands of many thousands of local school boards, whose members seldom qualify as educational experts. State control is slight and Federal assistance is rejected. We therefore are at an impasse. It is exceedingly difficult and time consuming to convince thousands of school boards that they must change the curriculum of the local high school; to persuade forty-eight states that their colleges and universities ought to confine themselves to education and not to vocational training and service activities which have no place in institutions of higher learning; or for that matter to win over thousands of alumni on whose bounty our privately endowed colleges and universities so largely depend.

"In no other Western country are educational institutions so precariously placed financially, so dependent on local politicians, on the whim of small communities where few have ever had a higher education. Half our colleges are continuously threatened with bankruptcy. The future looks bleak unless in some way Federal assistance can be made acceptable and some sort of national standard can be established to which diploma and degree-giving institutions must conform."

If we have now developed a real understanding and appreciation even of the dollars-and-cents value of science, it should be possible to get Congressional approval and public support of the necessary Constitutional amendment to provide for the establishment of such positions. Besides the direct administrative value, this kind of recognition would give added prestige to these fields and this should help with many of our current education and recruitment problems. Such steps would also reflect favorably on our government in other ways. For in this move we would be indicating that, at last, we were recognizing the deeper implications of science. Europeans have long criticized us for our failures in this respect. The step would indicate that the U.S. was maturing culturally, but most important the President and the Administration and Congress would gain the benefit of the full collaboration of American science in reaching major policy decisions and then in carrying them out.

If it is desirable to have scientists represented in the upper executive and legislative levels of the national government, it is also desirable to take similar steps at state and local levels of government as well. Perhaps more of our large businesses should look around the table at their Board of Directors meetings. Those who see no scientists sitting there might be wise to consider what would happen if they were to add some "green grass" thinkers to their Boards.

CHAPTER III

SCIENCE HOUSEKEEPING

Almost every human activity, whether it is maintaining a home or a symphony orchestra, has housekeeping problems. Though many of them seem rather dull, boring and sometimes even disagreeable, most of us know they cannot long be neglected without damaging the quality of the service or product—perhaps even destroying it. Millions of broken homes, bankrupt businesses and defunct organizations sadly prove this basic point.

There is considerable evidence that many of the present day problems of science are the result of poor housekeeping. As we have seen, science has grown from simple beginnings when it was generally a part-time hobby of men who earned their living as doctors, engineers, pharmacists or teachers. Except in a few instances, it was the full-time occupation of only a few well-to-do men who could participate in it without thought of economic reward. In those earlier days, scientific organizations were essentially club-groups in which the few members met for interesting conversation, lectures, and demonstrations. The housekeeping problems were extremely simple.

In the short span of about a hundred years, science has indeed become the very bedrock on which our modern society rests. In doing so it has become a professional way of life for many thousands of men and women. However, science is still organized in effect as a hobby instead of as a profession. The housekeeping methods of professional science organizations have not kept pace with the expanded responsibilities resulting from this evolution. It is a failure which is at the heart of the crisis which faces us.

The major activities of most science organizations have been the publication of their journals, the holding of national meetings, and the conduct of a few symposia, conferences and small special meetings. These activities are planned by the national officers and carried out by the paid executive staff. The rank and file membership have little to do with these matters except to attend them. Of course these societies have committees of members which serve as advisers to the officers of the organization or as liaison bodies that keep in touch with other agencies. Through such experiences many of our science leaders have come to realize the larger potentials of science which are being missed today. But these administrative activities are so remote from the immediate concerns of most members that they receive little, if any, attention from them. Few scientists take an active part in the housekeeping affairs of the societies to which they belong. Therefore, they fail to learn from first hand experience the potential value of increasing the role of these organizations in the formulation of public policies. Naturally the activities of our scientific associations remain almost exclusively devoted to the "enjoyment" of science, the reading, publishing and discussion of papers, just as in the days when science was only a hobby. The few science leaders who see these possibilities do not have the financial or organizational support to do much about them, except talk. And not very many are listening when they do talk. The situation is frozen and our scientific housekeeping is not being done properly.

What are the main organizational housekeeping functions which business administrators, economists and management experts recognize—the functions which every organization must perform? How well are our professional science organizations carrying out these functions?

Organization: The first function of an organization is to organize —to decide who is "boss," who does what, when the major activities will take place, who will pay for them, who will be responsible for seeing that they get done, and what the penalties will be for failure. These organizational decisions must be made in every well run home, club or business. They are not always written out, sometimes they are not even stated. Often they may merely be assumed. You will find they exist, at least in microcosm, in any efficient organization. In athletic teams, the "take charge" player may be the hub of such decisions and therefore the key man of a successful team. In large, complex business, government and service organizations, formal, written rules and policies are necessary to integrate and coordinate the actions of the many individuals involved and the relations of these organizations to others.

That our science has essentially no such internal organization is obvious. It has never even recognized that a need exists for the various science societies to confederate in order to perform more effectively their rightful role of policy advisers to our government. Except for the National Research Council and the National Academy of Sciences which are not exclusively organs of the scientific societies,

but are quasi-government institutions, there are no organizations of
the type I have in mind. The federal government has developed a
number of science organizations—the National Science Foundation,
the National Bureau of Standards, and the National Institutes of
Health—to name only a few. These are necessarily organs of the
federal government. Their relations with scientists and their professional societies are good, but they do not work for independent
science; they work for government. The scientists associated with
government agencies must give these agencies their first loyalty—
only secondarily are they able to be concerned with science as such.
This is natural and is not to be criticized. But this leaves the broad
professional interests of scientists and the general public's interest
in science poorly represented, if at all.

Most of the professional societies of scientists themselves are
of a highly specialized nature. They usually relate to a specific
division or subdivision of knowledge. Their membership is generally
small. Because of this, and the low economic status of scientists
as well, their societies are usually not well supported financially.
Consequently, they are handicapped in performing those direct personal services for their members that win the kind of loyalty that
pays off for the treasuries of other organizations. Most national
scientific societies are not organized to be run democratically
through broad membership participation. Because they do not
play much of a direct role in the individual's economic or professional
life most members have little interest in their administration. Organizational control of most societies usually rests in a small self-
perpetuating group because the rest of the members have no great
interest in anything other than the purely scientific activities of
these organizations. There is usually little encouragement to those
outside these inner cliques to try to join them. The situation is the
product of a series of interacting, vicious circles, all operating to pre-
clude science from playing its rightful role in building a better America and a better world.

Personnel: Every organization has personnel interests. Science's
personnel interests should be of two main types.

The first main interest is that of helping its members remain usefully occupied in jobs which are congenial to them both professionally
and economically as long as they wish to work. It should do this job
so well that the second job, recruiting young scientists, would require nothing more than the simplest kind of "bulletin board" services
to help bring people and jobs into contact. The work lives of prac-

ticing scientists should appear sufficiently attractive for adequate numbers of young people to be drawn to science without the necessity of elaborate recruitment programs.

Many senior as well as young scientists have job problems. It would improve the morale of scientists in general if mechanisms existed for helping such individuals find adequate solutions to job problems as quickly as possible. Science has not developed good machinery for accomplishing this, at least for some of our older men who are currently trying to find new jobs after being retired from the ones in which they had worked most of their lives—retired on pensions so small they cannot decently survive on them. The American Association of University Professors, which opened a Washington office in 1958, was the first organization to take real action on this problem. And the Aging Committee of the National Social Welfare Assembly has recently undertaken an extensive study of the matter.

It is alleged that there are thousands of empty jobs waiting for scientists, researchers or educators, but there is apparently great difficulty in fitting a far smaller number of people into this much larger number of jobs. A good housekeeper should care more about and have the machinery to know more about and do more about this problem than most of science does at present.

Youthful Recruitment: Most businesses have developed a recruitment program to maintain their organizational vitality. Science has only recently begun to recognize and consider this problem. This is a clear reflection of "club" psychology. Clubs don't recruit members; people ask to join. Because science has been so limited in its housekeeping organization, it has no official forum for consideration of its recruitment problems. As a result, many individual voices have been raised but no well-organized continuing study or analysis has been going on. Many are talking, but few are listening. Naturally, under these circumstances, science as such is doing very little that is effective. Talk, without decision, plans, coordination and action, accomplishes little.

Science's Collection of Internal Operational (Administrative) Information: Social organizations, unlike biological ones, are not born with nervous systems. Large social organizations have to build their own systems for collecting data on the activities of their peripheral sub-units and individual members. Such a system is as vital as the nerves and brain of a human being. If properly designed, it need be no more cumbersome or wasteful than a good nervous system.

At present our science in general, and the special scientific societies, collect almost no information on their members or on their activities which could provide the kind of information necessary for intelligent planning of the business of the associations or as guides for advising government or others about such matters. The simple rosters of the Scientific Manpower Commission, valuable as they no doubt are, fall woefully short of providing the kind of data which should be available on so important a subject. We have more complete vital statistics on purebred cattle and horses than on our scientists. The available statistical information on the economic status of scientists is so meager that quantitative discussion is almost impossible.

There is no well organized effort being made to collect and analyze data on the professional aspects of science or on the growth and development of different areas of science. It isn't as though there is no necessity for this kind of information. Such information is required to guide us right now in formulating personnel and other policies and for estimating future scientific growth and the educational and other needs which will result therefrom. For example, every committee which writes a recruitment pamphlet must face this problem and "guess" about the quantitative needs for scientists in the future. When you don't even have good data on the present situation, this makes future "guessing" quite hazardous to say the least. Can we advise youngsters indiscriminately to enter a field of work unless we are pretty sure there will still be a field open to all of them when they are ready to enter it? As an illustration of what uninformed recruitment "guessing" can lead to, consider the thousands of veterans of World War II who were encouraged, by various agencies, to become "family farmers"—a way of life that today leads only to bankruptcy in most areas of the country. How many youngsters are today being recruited into fields in which jobs will be gone or overcrowded by the time they are ready for them? Even with wise planning, mistakes can be made in vocational recruitment, but science should develop a nationally coordinated system for studying the present and past and estimating the future. This would do for science something similar to what the President's economic advisers do with regard to the economy in general. The system should be independent of government and its actions and recommendations should be known to the general public and so be open to the corrective influence of public criticism.

We should also develop a system for maintaining up-to-date records of the professional activities and development of individual members. These personnel records could serve many useful purposes for the professional advancement of individuals, as well as provide the general statistical data just discussed. I will discuss this topic in more detail in a later chapter.

Science's Communication Business: The ultimate products of basic science are useful new ideas, which each special group publishes in its journal. These journals are fundamentally tools for communicating important scientific ideas from one scientist to another. They are no longer club "news-letters" for reporting items of interest to a few members. They contain vital information of indirect interest to a very wide audience. Since basic science has little direct money value it places basic science at a great disadvantage if its journals must operate as non-subsidized businesses, supported mainly by advertising revenue and the subscriptions of the relatively few members who are directly concerned. Because of this poor economic foundation most basic science journals, essential though they are, now operate on "cheese paring" budgets. They are trying to break even at such low circulation levels that their advertising rates are pitifully small. The medical and engineering journals written primarily for applied scientists, doctors and engineers, who buy and sell the products of industry, have no difficulty selling advertising.

In our desire to stimulate interest in basic science, it would be desirable if our science journals could give subscriptions to all the high schools and perhaps to elementary schools also. They might also give them to young scientists in out-of-the-way spots isolated from libraries. But of course they can't afford to do this.

I am confident that those who want to stimulate youngsters to enter science could get the most recruits per dollar spent by providing free subscriptions to at least 15 or 20 basic science magazines for all our high schools. It would also be helpful in maintaining and stimulating the interests of scientists in general if "magazine subscription scholarships" could be provided free, if not to all at least to those isolated from adequate library facilities. This increased circulation would perhaps justify increased advertising rates and the present adverse business cycle of basic science journals might be broken. Even if the subsidy had to be continued indefinitely, the prime function of the basic science journals—the communication of ideas—would be improved at a cost which would be a tiny fraction of our total science budget.

Production, Storage and Distribution of Scientific Knowledge: Un-

like most tangible products the products of basic science—ideas—
have no "shelf-life." As soon as they are born they become old, but
they never completely lose their value. We seldom if ever throw an
idea away. They often get repackaged, like a woman with a new
hair-do, and thereby seem almost new, and as fresh and valuable
as ever. For this reason the "idea" shelf-space keeps growing. For
some time, the shelf-space has been growing at the rate of about 5 per
cent per year. Such a rapid rate of growth calls for new methods
and principles of storage and distribution. The introduction of new
methods and principles of idea storage requires housekeeping decisions which can only be made by *organized* science. Problems of
nomenclature and classification and similar matters cannot be satis-
factorily imposed from the top—even if there were a "top." Such
matters are best solved after widespread discussions which clarify the
problems in hand and lead to general agreement on their broad aspects. But as we have seen, science is not organized to consider or
decide such matters. Individuals who have tried to solve pieces of
these problems meet with little success for solution so often hinges
on group cooperation. This can only be obtained if the group partici-
pates in some degree in formulating the solution. As I will show in
a later chapter, the technical aspects of the literature problem are
really not too difficult. The real crux of the matter is that no one has
the authority to speak for science as a whole—and science itself is
not organized to consider and decide such questions with the necessary unanimity and authority.

So, while we are widely aware of our communication deficiencies,
little is done to correct the fundamental cause. Meanwhile the products of science, "ideas," are becoming increasingly difficult to locate
because of the antiquated storage and distribution machinery still
in use—machinery which can be modernized only if we approach
this problem as an organized group in the manner outlined above.

The untidy housekeeping of science also shows up in the fact that
the recruitment of new young scientists has been falling off, thus
threatening the actual life of American science and ultimately of
American society itself. The low economic status of scientists, which
surely has a great effect on recruitment, is a sympton of our failure
to adopt the measures which medicine and other professions have
developed to meet their similar needs. Criticizing public attitudes
will accomplish nothing. We had better look to ourselves for solutions.

As I have pointed out, the National Science Foundation, the National Bureau of Standards, the National Institutes of Health, even the National Research Council and the National Academy of Sciences are basically organs of government. They are supported by government and their first job is to serve the needs of government. Many public and scientific leaders have encouraged us to believe that business, or the foundations, or aroused public opinion, can and will solve the problems of science. They can't and they won't. Science needs to strengthen and coordinate its own organizations. It must define its own needs. It must formulate programs for meeting its needs and be organized to pay for, work for, and, if necessary, fight for its own programs just as labor, industry, and the other professions have long since done. If science is to assume its rightful role as one of the major forces helping to shape the future of our society, then it must come of age, learn how to be a better housekeeper and accept the responsibilities that always accompany power. It must become as modern in its business methods and organization as it is in its laboratory methods and development. However unhappy it may make some people, scientists included, the political realities make it clear that independent science must enter the field of politics, develop policy-making organs and lobby for what *it* wants. Today the "unrepresented" are actually represented negatively by other lobbyists who are available and pushing their clients' aims, often at the expense of the best interest of science.

CHAPTER IV

HOW FREE IS AMERICAN SCIENCE?

Everyone assumes the American scientist is free and unfettered—but is he?

We are so used to thinking of the United States as a democratic country that it is assumed almost every aspect of our life—including our science—is also democratic. As proof of our freedom, we are reminded that we can call the President of the United States "a bum" if we want to. Even if we accept the idea that this is adequate proof of our political freedom, it still leaves open the matter of economic and scientific freedom. Most scientists and teachers work for a salary in a public or quasi-public institution. Therefore, their job continuance is subject to the continuing approval of the directors of those institutions. And the directors are subject to many kinds of political pressure. In recent years we have seen many examples in which teachers and scientists, some even with tenure rights, were forced from jobs by institutional directors to whom political pressures were applied. Many who lost their jobs had not been proved technically incompetent or guilty of crime. If we want our teachers and scientists to have the full freedom needed to keep our educational and scientific organizations in good health, we must restore the "right to criticize." This right can exist only if the job of any one who wishes to criticize is protected from administrative reprisals for exercising it. Hence maximum scientific freedom requires *both* political and economic freedom.

Senior faculty members, generally full professors, have long been supposed to have guaranteed permanent job tenure in most schools; tenure which could be lost only if the individual was convicted of crime. Incidentally the freedom to be legally impartial is guaranteed for our judges by the same permanent tenure device. This "right" is intended to provide the economic freedom on which academic and scientific freedom rest. The McCarthy era made a myth of that "right," and it will take a long time to restore confidence in it. The American Association of University Professors is powerless to stop the onslaught, which has made a farce of the concept of tenure rights.

To bring the issue of freedom down to specifics, let us ask: How free is the average teacher or scientist to criticize the plans or policies of higher officers of his university or institution? What machinery exists for an individual to criticize a policy or plan with which he may disagree? Are teachers or scientists free to demand an open hearing on a plan or policy with which they may disagree, unless they are prepared to resign their jobs?

Because guaranteed tenure is of such fundamental importance to free education, free science and a free society and since existing safeguards have proved inadequate to protect it, perhaps some kind of strong federal legal support—a sort of "Educational and Scientific Bill of Rights"—should be enacted to safeguard this economic freedom of teachers, scientists, and administrators of educational and scientific institutions in the future. We cannot have a healthy science and healthy education until the morale of teachers is restored. Some such step seems needed to restore it.

And what about the internal economic aspects of research support? How does this affect the freedom of the scientists? A large part of government research funds spent for "defense" research goes to various private companies which do much of the work on a cost-plus-fixed-fee basis. Much of this is similar to ordinary business developmental research, with fairly specific objectives. I have heard it argued persuasively, by men with first-hand knowledge, that this system, at least when applied to "defense" research, encourages many expensive inefficiencies. Others defend the system with equal vigor. Since my first-hand knowledge of research is in the medical and biological and related fields, I shall limit my comments to these areas. This research is supported in a more or less uniform way. The funds available are distributed by a few government agencies or private foundations and, with only slight differences, they all follow similar administration policies and procedures. They generally divide the scientific field with which they are concerned into a number of study sections. In the medical area, this division into sections may be on a pathology or disease basis, on an anatomical basis, on a physiological basis, or on some combination of the three. These study sections have executive secretaries to receive the requests and to handle the paper work involved in the fund-allocation procedure, and committees of special consultants who advise on the scientific merits of the grant requests.

Grant requests received by the agencies are assigned to one or another of the various study sections. This assignment is an administrative decision which may, for example, place a proposal in a pathology category though its author's major focus was really physiology. To some extent, such errors are inherent in any classification system, and perhaps are not often of critical importance. It is difficult to know.

Each section has a committee of specialists serving as consultants to the director of the agency. One or more times a year, the specialists meet to consider the grant requests which have accumulated. If, as is often the case, the number of requests is large in relation to the number of consultants, then a further sub-division takes place and each consultant personally considers only a fraction of the total requests before the committee. He then serves as the adviser to the whole committee on his fraction of the total requests. If there is plenty of money to go around, there are no serious money-distribution problems with which to deal. The only problems then are to decide whether the projects for which money is requested are worth doing, whether the individuals requesting the funds have the facilities and the capabilities and the drive to do them, etc. While these are difficult problems, they are simple compared to the situation which obtains when money is limited and it is necessary to decide—on paper evidence alone—which of several competing requests are to be accepted and which rejected. If these consultants are like other humans some of them may harbor scientific or even personal prejudices which could influence their judgments about such requests.

A complicating aspect is that these consultants are themselves operating scientists, sometimes with grant requests of their own, or of close colleagues, before the very committees on which they serve. In short, these men are in scientific competition to some degree with those whose grant requests they are called on to consider.

Can anyone argue that this is the best of all possible ways to distribute research funds? Is the scientist who is dependent on these agencies for the funds to support his research, the funds without which he cannot work, free to criticize the people involved in the decision process? Can he compete with them scientifically on a basis of real equality? Of course, in practice, the applicant does not even have a basis for criticism of grant decisions. He is simply given an award or he is refused. He is not told the reason for either decision, much less the reasons other competitive grant requests were accepted or rejected. I am not implying that he should be; the paper work involved in trying to do so would be fantastic. I am merely describing the existing situation.

It is sometimes argued that mistakes, misjudgments, and even, perhaps, deliberate unfairness, cause no serious problem in the operation of these systems because we have a large number of agencies dispensing funds. Hence there are a number of different committees to which one may apply for support. If the applicant is turned down one place, he simply tries another. The trouble with that argument is that, to a large extent, the same men serve as consultants in all the agencies in their field. Therefore, you may be refused more than once by the same man. Not only that, but these men are top scientific administrators, and thus control the professional societies, the journals, and the job and other opportunities in their fields as well.

Our scientific leaders have a lot of power. Much of it is indirect and ill-defined. It operates almost entirely behind closed doors, with no public appeal mechanisms whatsoever. Of course, most of the specialist consultants are people of the highest integrity who are doing their best to make a poor administrative system work. It is a tribute to them that it has worked as well as it has. Nevertheless, the "project" system, an administrative device which continuously keeps investigators under the necessity of maintaining the favorable personal opinion of other scientists in order to keep their laboratories running, does limit scientific freedom in an undesirable and unnecessary way.

Freedom is an active state, not a passive one. And, of course, freedom in science as in other affairs today cannot be unlimited. The real test of freedom in modern, complex society must be this: *Is there an organized, official channel through which the lowliest individual in the organization may protest any decision of those officials above him administratively, without suffering a reprisal for his action?* Soap box freedom may have therapeutic value for the individual. It has little value for society. If scientists and teachers want real organized freedom they must do a number of things. They must develop their national professional societies into effective instruments capable of speaking with authority for the membership. This can be accomplished only by the societies' developing strong regional and local subdivisions. It is not necessary here to try to detail the form of this decentralization. It is only important to stress that those organizations which are successful in maintaining the interest and support of their "grass roots" members are the ones whose local meetings and activities serve local interests and benefit the ordinary members. This means emphasis on educational, economic and social activities. Scientists must also take an active role in interpreting science to the general public and to their own trustees, visitors, and administrative officers.

The grant-in-aid-of-projects system must be abolished as the principal means of supporting basic research. It must be replaced by institutional grants, and by life-long grants-in-aid of investigators with guaranteed tenure and decent retirement a part of the arrangement. It is the only way to provide basic scientists with the economic and scientific freedom necessary for maximum productivity. The basis for this opinion will be developed more fully in a later chapter.

Another aspect of this matter, though a subtle one, is nevertheless of great importance. When you operate a science program on the competitive grant-in-aid basis in which each project must be evaluated (and generally reevaluated) each year, you introduce a kind of "marketing" psychology into the situation. This overemphasizes competition. It does not produce the ideal atmosphere to encourage the free flow of ideas, the kind of atmosphere in which basic science has flourished most successfully. Basic science is far more cooperative than competitive. Both elements are desirable. Our effort should always be to maintain a proper balance between the two motivations.

Everything said in this chapter points in a single direction: Many of our scientists are *not* scientifically free in a real and practical sense. The man who must temper his remarks by consideration for his job, for the support of his laboratory, for his own continued opportunity to do research, is not entirely free to follow truth wherever it leads. He is in danger of becoming an "Organization Man", and his scientific thoughts—especially his public statements—will be influenced by this fact. Such a man will be forced to think too much about the administrative problems he faces, at the expense of the scientific problems he is supposed to be solving.

In recent years, we have begun in this country to take some tentative cognizance of these facts. We have set up a few "established investigatorships." But for how long are they "established?" The longest, in most cases, is five years. These researchers do not know who will be on the committee to review their "established" arrangement at the end of five years. Will the new review people have similar interests and consider the work involved as important as the present committee does? God knows!

This is not to argue for life-time guaranteed jobs for anyone and everyone who can get a degree and call himself a scientist. But it is to suggest that we find some better solution than we have. There are sensible, realistic ways by which senior scientists can evaluate junior scientists. There are many existing precedents to be found in European countries which can be studied to learn better administrative ways of arriving at these decisions fairly, and with reasonable accuracy. Surely ways can be found of establishing life-time jobs which will not fill our laboratories with men looking for lifetime hand-outs. It is generally not conducive to the efficiency of a scientist to have to pull up stakes every few years and reestablish himself in a new laboratory. Probably the most productive scientists are those who have pretty stable work arrangments. Surely if a mechanism for selecting "Life-time Investigators" were properly established there would be few who would fail to be scientifically productive.

There are also "freedom" problems in connection with "teams". In building many of our scientific "teams", we have drifted into some errors about "group think." The success of the Manhattan project in making an A-bomb has created the erroneous impression that the Manhattan physicists discovered the A-bomb. They did not. The essence of the A-bomb, the basic scientific ideas, existed in many minds some time before Einstein wrote the famous letter which made President Roosevelt *aware* of the possibility of making one.

The Manhattan project which then followed was a "crash" developmental project handled in a hastily-organized, Army-style "team" fashion. All the mature scientists who worked on it know that it was a wildly inefficient and excessively expensive way to solve the problem. But the stakes were so high that this seemed justified. But we ignored the fact that this was a "crash" program. We let this set a pattern, and now a good deal of our science effort is "operating" on this regimented, over-centralized, inefficient basis. The Manhattan project seems to have deluded us into believing that "group think" works in science. As someone has so aptly said, it has led some people to the conclusion that if it takes one woman nine months to create a baby, nine women can unite in a "team" to produce a baby in a month.

Over-centralization has now progressed to such a point, in many cases, that the needs of the scientists are, to a large extent, made subservient to the needs of the administrators who are supposed to be "helping and serving" them. This seems true not only in Government laboratories, but in many of our universities, foundations, and hospitals. There is no reason for forming large organizations to do basic research. "Teams" can do some kinds of applied research.

Certain complex problems must be handled the "team" way. But generally speaking, teams do nothing but hamper basic research. There are exceptional problems where a large basic problem may be subdivided and a coordinated attack made by several groups *cooperating*. This is not the kind of "team" I am criticizing.

We should establish the following general rule concerning basic research institutes: *No scientific institution should be so large that its director will not be able to know personally all of the people in the top two or three echelons. He should also know the essence of what is going on in every laboratory of his institute.* Such a rule should go a long way to protect us from developing "teams" whose first job seems to be to make work to keep their administrators on a payroll.

Secrecy and security have received most of the criticism in connection with the question of scientific freedom. Secrecy is charged with having caused serious delays in our defense research. It is easy to see why this is true when basic research is involved. Anything which impedes the flow of relevant basic ideas must delay the ultimate solution. It is purely a quantitative matter.

A useful way to look at the discovery of new ideas in basic research is in terms of a jig-saw puzzle. But the "Nature-puzzle" differs from real ones in several ways. First of all many of her "pieces" have not yet been found. Also when new "pieces" are found, they often are "rough" and only after considerable "shaping" and "polishing" are their true values learned. Sometimes they do not fit well with the other parts till this improvement has occurred. Newton's law of gravity and even Darwin's theory of evolution are examples of "pieces" that have been worked over and improved many times and thus made to fit more and more parts of the "puzzle". Of course, "pieces" are sometimes discovered which seem to be isolated from the main puzzle, but sooner or later if they are true "pieces" their position in the puzzle will be found. Now the "fitting" and the "shaping" and the "polishing" usually are greatly facilitated by direct communication between the many players. If the "players" of the "Nature-puzzle" are not permitted to "see" the pieces of others "playing" in their puzzle-area, it is not difficult to see that the game soon loses much of its zest and its pace is likely to slow down.

Secret research is comparable to the latter situation. Only a very few people are permitted to know everything. Therefore, the pleasure of the search is limited and so the pace of the game is almost sure to slow down as in the illustration. That this takes the enjoyment out of research was clearly stated in a January, 1958, article in *The*

Reporter magazine, entitled "The High Cost of Scientific Secrecy." This article quoted Dr. Harold Urey, Nobel prize winner and an important member of the Manhattan project, to this effect: "At the end of the war, I looked very definitely for some things to do that would not enter into the classified field, and the things which I found to do are as far away from defense things as they could possibly be. Thus, determining the temperatures in the ancient oceans is not likely to become a classified subject, so far as I can see. . . . I may say that selection of such subjects was done definitely with some thought in mind of having some work to do which I could talk about freely without worrying about the question of classification at all."

The only atmosphere in which basic science can flourish is one in which scientists are assumed to be competent, honest and loyal till they give direct evidence to the contrary and which permits a high degree (not unlimited) of open communication. Our present security programs are built on the opposite premises. Secrecy may be vital in certain areas even of basic research and it may not slow down pure developmental research too badly. But basic research cannot possibly flourish in secrecy, for the fundamental rules of the game are violated by it. The cost of secrecy is bound to be high in these areas.

No discussion of scientific freedom in the U.S. today would be complete which did not also consider the situation in the U.S.S.R. Writing in *Science*, Dr. Freeman Dyson, who visited the Soviet Union in 1956 as an exchange physicist, discussed the degree of freedom he observed there:

"Now, the editor of the (Baltimore) *Sun* asks me a question. He says, 'It is commonly stated by men of science that freedom is essential to a healthy scientific climate. And yet we learn from members of your group that Russian science, which surely had to put up with security arrangements more stringent than ours, is in a flourishing condition, and that Russian scientists show evidence of the highest morale in their personal and scientific life. How can this be so?' He invites me to set down my thoughts about this question. And I am happy to do so, because the question is a real and important one. . . Russian work in physics is now essentially free. I am not speaking here about political freedom. This, of course, does not exist in Russia, and will not exist in the foreseeable future. But a reasonable scientific freedom does now exist. That is to say, Russian physicists enjoy the basic professional freedoms, to work on problems of their own choosing, to publish their results, and to discuss their ideas with foreign colleagues. These freedoms are restricted by security rules which are similar to ours, perhaps slightly stricter. . . . The freedom of Russian science is quite new. It came suddenly, soon after the death of Stalin. Until two years ago, nothing whatever was published of experimental work in nuclear physics. . . . It is clear that the Soviet Government now understands the fact, which the American Government always knew, that scientific progress demands scientific freedom. It is also clear that the Soviet Government is spending enormous amounts of money on pure science, and seriously intends to make Moscow the scientific capital of the world. They have understood that the power of American science depends on America freely and openly attracting people and ideas from all over the world. And they intend now to beat us at our own game."

Dr. Lloyd V. Berkner, one of our top scientific administrators, has also commented on the relationship of science and government policy in the U.S.S.R. as follows: "The advantage to be acquired from emphasis on science and technology has led to subordination of Communist doctrine to science when the two conflict. The battle between the theory of relativity and Communism was short-lived—science won. Lysenko triumphed briefly in the struggle over predetermination in genetics, but he was then repudiated and Soviet genetics is recovering. These are indications that where science and Communism conflict, the present Soviet leadership is willing to subordinate political doctrine to science—an extraordinary spectacle in a totalitarian state."

It is, of course, futile to attempt direct comparison of the two countries in this or any other respect. However, these quotations seem to be significant because they indicate that the present Soviet leaders have come to appreciate the high costs of excessive secrecy. It is to be hoped that the many criticisms of our own security system, when considered along with the obviously high costs of secrecy, will lead us to greatly reduce the area of secrecy. This will be another, but probably not the most important, of several steps proposed here for enhancing the freedom of our scientists.

Chapter V

THE SEARCH FOR THE GIFTED

There is growing concern over the large number of children in this country who have superior native intelligence but do not go on to college. We hear pleas from many sources that we encourage and aid these "gifted" children. Although college enrollments are higher today than ever before, the needs of our society demand far more citizens with scientifically and technically-educated brains. We are now concerning ourselves about a situation that most of us have largely ignored for too long. Soviet competition has at last made us aware that we can no longer afford to waste any of our precious brain-power.

What shall we do?

Many problems are involved. Some of the major questions to consider are these:

Who are the "gifted" children? Who are the "superior" children? Are they the same?

How can we identify the "gifted" and/or "superior" children?

Should we concentrate our "best" teachers in order to teach the "gifted" and/or "superior" children?

Should we segregate the "gifted" and/or "superior" children and "best" teachers in special schools?

Is it necessary to identify and guide the "gifted" and/or "superior" children? Is it better merely to create a desire for worth-while goals and let children find their own ways to reach them? How accurate must an I. Q. screen be?

It is quite clear that the average person makes little distinction between the terms "gifted" and "superior." But in educational circles, the terms are not synonymous. Since no official or standard definition exists, we can only say that the term "superior" children refers to a fairly large segment of our most intelligent children—a segment including from 1/5 to 1/3 of all children. The word "gifted" usually refers to a much smaller segment—no larger than the top five percent, and often as small as one percent or less. Dr. Florence N. Brumbaugh, a well-known educator interested in the "gifted," defines them as follows: "An arbitrary minimum I.Q. of 136 obtained from

scores of the Stanford-Binet Test, 1937 revision, is used for purpose
of identification since it represents the top one percent of the juvenile
population in general intelligence."

This definition implies that the sorting of children according
to their grades of intelligence is essentially no more complicated
than grading eggs. Unfortunately, many of the plans for testing, coun-
seling, guiding, and segregating our children accept this dangerously
over-simplified approach to the subject. We must examine this
matter very closely. It is far from simple.

Of course, we can identify the children who get scores of 136 or
better. The real problem is whether this arbitrary figure includes
all or even most of the children who will prove to be "gifted" adults.

The amazing fact is that we are being asked to accept this and
similar definitions though there is no scientific evidence to support
the idea that "gifted" adults always or nearly always had top-one percent I.Q. scores as children. In fact, such evidence as there is indicates
that a good many "gifted" adults of both the present and past, did
not have exceptionally high I.Q. scores in childhood. This is not to
deny that many superior adults did give evidence of their superiority
when they were children. The point of real interest is that a fairly
large number of highly successful, even "genius-type," adults *do not*
sparkle as children.

Many of the most serious students of these tests realize and admit
that I.Q. tests have serious limitations for measuring intelligence itself, let alone for measuring so elusive a quality as "giftedness." If
you ask such people this question, "Do I.Q. tests measure intelligence?" they will answer something like this: "They measure intelligence, in quotes. What they really measure is a *particular* individual's ability (provided he is motivated to do well) to answer a
particular set of questions that a *particular* psychologist has decided
are useful for testing and studying intelligence."

If you have taken an I.Q. test, you will recall the great emphasis
on word mastery and to a somewhat lesser extent the emphasis
placed on mathematics. Has it been demonstrated that intelligence
is possessed *only* by those who are facile with words and figures—
useful as these faculties are? There are serious reasons for doubting
this. Einstein and Edison, to name two, were not especially good
with word symbols. Many students of giftedness doubt that either of
these geniuses would have achieved high I.Q. scores in childhood.
Einstein is said not even to have been superior in mathematics. His
strongest faculty was his ability to imagine physical models of his

ideas. His mental image of an elevator rising so rapidly in space that a light coming through a hole in the front of it would be curved before it hit the back wall is his classical model on which the whole theory of relativity rests. Dr. Curt Richter, a well known research worker, has made the following pertinent comment on this point: "There are researchers who do not work on a verbal plane, who cannot put into words what they are doing—whose thinking functions in terms of experiences, subconscious observations—who don't know what they have been after until they actually arrive at their discoveries."

Haven't you known people who were not too articulate or people who could hardly add who, nevertheless, were highly successful in important activities? I have. I've never asked any of these people what their I.Q.'s were. It didn't seem to matter. Before we allow the I.Q. test to be used as a screen for segregating the "gifted" from the ungifted, we'd be smart to insist that the advocates of these tests give us the soundest kind of evidence that they are not going to screen out our future Edisons and Einsteins, cutting them off from the contacts they need to develop their hidden faculties.

What about speed? Most of the I.Q. tests require that you answer the questions in a limited amount of time. Since a premium is placed on speed, accuracy is, therefore, not the only consideration. But we may fairly ask, "Is speed a necessary ingredient of intelligence?" I have known some mighty wise and intelligent people who were certainly not quick in their mental reactions. I think quite a few of them would not achieve "gifted" I.Q. scores—at least not one percent "gifted," because they think too slowly. However, such people did very well indeed in making difficult decisions, imaginative suggestions and intelligent predictions.

We have found it useful to build vehicles of all shapes, sizes and speeds. If we want to move a pile of dirt, we use a bulldozer. It we want to haul something, we use a truck. If we want to go driving on a vacation trip, we like a sport car. If we used the over-simplified I.Q. approach, we'd try to solve all our transportation needs with sports cars. There are many places in science and life for many different models of intelligence.

It has been repeatedly and thoroughly demonstrated that both as a group and as individuals, children mature, physically and mentally, at different rates. The child who is alert, cooperative and intelligent at one phase of development may seem much less so at other stages. These growth fluctuations affect the I. Q. scores of the individual child to score as a one percent "gifted" one time and as not quite "gifted" at another. With the simple one percent definition, you only have to fall from 136 to 135 to shift from the "gifted" to the "ungifted" group.

Does the I. Q. vary in relation to factors other than physical growth and mental development? The answer is *yes*. It was demonstrated over 20 years ago (in some careful studies made at Iowa University) that the environment of children greatly affected their I.Q. scores. Children surrounded by dull-witted adults, whose I. Q. scores placed them at the "feeble-minded" level, often raised their scores to normal levels when they were placed in normal foster homes.

In another study, an orphanage was divided into two equal groups of children whose average I.Q. scores were the same. One group received the stimulus of attending nursery school each day. The other group did not. The average I.Q. in the nursery school group continued to rise at the rates of normal children. But the unstimulated group's average I. Q. score failed to increase.

There are numerous studies which have shown that psychologically disturbed children often make poorer scores than they do later when their psychological problems have been relieved.

Surely all this evidence casts grave doubt on the practical value of I.Q. tests for accurately screening out those individuals who are "gifted." The evidence indicates a great deal of imprecision in these tests even when used as a tool for measuring the same individual's intelligence at different times or under changed conditions. It is a safe tool only in the hands of well-organized psychologists who clearly understand the limitations of such tests.

To give another example showing how difficult this whole problem is, let us consider this: Our medical schools have for a number of years been using elaborate screening procedures—I.Q. tests, medical aptitude tests and other criteria—to select their new students. These tests are given after two or three years of college. The aim of the tests is to help identify those most likely to be good doctors. The accuracy of these tests was recently analyzed. It was discovered that this elaborate testing and weighing procedure (far more extensive than can possibly be done on a nation-wide scale) was only 60 percent correct in predicting the class grade position of those chosen for medical training.

Graduates of tiny Reed College have earned proportionately more doctoral degrees than those of any other American college. Reed has had a higher ratio of Rhodes scholarship winners than any other

U.S. college. It has proportionately more men in Who's Who than any other American college. Reed does not limit its enrollment to those applicants with absolute top high school grades. It tries to consider the whole background of each applicant, and it takes some youngsters with low high school marks. The policy has been proven sound, for some of Reed's brightest science scholarship winners are those who received poor grades in high school.

Dr. Catherine Cox Miles, one of the best known and most thorough students of the psychology of the "gifted," says this:

"It has not been said, nor does serious consideration of the complexity of intellect, motivation, and other personality factors, lead investigators to suppose that the measure of intelligence alone can serve fully to predict later social or intellectual accomplishment or creative achievement . . . The gifted child defined in intelligence test terms may not be the adult genius. The latter combines with high mental ability traits of personality and in many cases also special talents, not necessarily closely correlated with intelligence . . . Intelligence is an important factor in accomplishment, but it proves to be only one factor among others, perhaps many others."

A recently completed study by Drs. Dale M. Yocum and Kenneth E. Anderson adds important confirmation to the arguments given above. These men studied the "exceptional" students who entered Kansas University in 1954. They studied those whose entrance test scores or subsequent grades were either among the top or bottom 10% of the total group. They gave these "exceptional" students four tests—a psychological test, a mathematics test, and two different English tests. The investigators found that of the 1210 sudents, only two scored in the top 10% in all tests. A considerable number of the "top" 10% scored in the bottom 10% in some tests, and also in some of their actual classroom grades. Only six individuals were in the bottom 10% of all scores, showing that, generally, inferiority was also rare in this group.

Their major conclusion was this: College students who are *generally* superior in ability are very scarce. But so also are college students who are *generally* inferior.

The statement by Dr. Miles, the experience of Reed College and the Kansas study all substantiate the common-sense view that I.Q. tests measure only one aspect of a very complex set of variables which enter into the development of those adults who demonstrate intellectual superiority.

Now let us consider the following questions: *Should we concentrate our "best" teachers in order to teach the "gifted" and/or "superior" children? Should we segregate the "gifted" and/or "superior" children in special schools—physically separate from those which the remaining children attend?*

At what age or at what grade level should we test and segregate the children, if we were going to do so? We know that intellectual growth fluctuates, just as physical growth does. We have seen that I.Q. scores fluctuate with emotional swings—and all children pass through them. We have already considered the great importance of a stimulating environment for increasing I.Q. scores. With all these variables, how can one select a time for giving these tests which will be suitable for correctly and fairly detecting the *true* top 1%? The answer is that there is no single suitable time. If tests were repeated every year for several years on the same children, the chances are the top 1% would be a slightly different group each time.

On the other hand, attempts to make a continuing and complicated screen will cost too much to be practical, even if it were sufficiently accurate. Though no one can estimate the cost of these schemes until they are carefully described, it is clear that a really extensive screen (with a battery of several tests) would be very costly to apply to all our children. It is even doubtful that we have enough good psychologists to conduct such a program properly.

Since we already know that lack of adequate stimulation is a strong deterrent to the development of intellectual interests in many children, our schools should have as one of their major goals the objective of providing such stimulation for all children. Segregation of the "gifted" students and the "best" teachers into separate special schools will hardly further this goal. Segregation of the "gifted" will have a most adverse effect on the school environment in the "ungifted" schools and further limit the development of those youngsters, from unstimulating homes, who could greatly profit from contact with their more intellectually-alert schoolmates. Segregation which puts the "gifted" in special schools with the "best" teachers is certainly a formula for making the competition of life turn out the way the I.Q. scores predict. It would "stack the deck" on a grand scale.

Let us consider what it would do to our society to segregate and educate a "gifted" elite in such a way. Those not chosen would consider themselves "ungifted" whether you called them "Eager Beavers" or "Brownies" or "Space Children." They would not be so stupid that they wouldn't notice that their "gifted" neighbor went to a different school. This would be an additional psychic burden for a child supposedly already handicapped by nature. Many young people with less than perfect physical equipment become champions through competing with those who at first were their superiors. It is probable that at least an important number of our "mental champions" also had less than perfect mental equipment to start with. At any rate what's wrong with a little mental as well as physical competition?

Such a system would more or less guarantee that none of the unidentified "gifted"—the Einstein and Edison types—would be able to develop themselves adequately, for it would restrict the quality of their educational opportunities. The fact that Einstein and Edison did not get good grades in school does not indicate that they were unstimulated by their school experience. It seems more likely that they were simply very thoughtful, perhaps somewhat slow, but obviously very deep thinkers. Surely these arguments indicate how greatly we may damage our educational system by sub-dividing it into "gifted" and "ungifted" systems, and how dangerous it would be to do so.

Intelligence tests, unfortunately, have been placed in the hands of some who are quite ignorant of their limitations. In the existing climate, these tests are being uncritically accepted because they seem to be panaceas. Certainly before any wide-scale national testing and I.Q.-based segregation of children is undertaken, a thorough airing of this whole subject is indicated.

The same adverse psychological factors also apply to the teachers, for these plans all suggest that the "best" teachers be reserved for the "gifted" students. Incidentally, will we call the "poor" teachers "Eager Beaver" or "Brownie" teachers to maintain their egos?

Let us now look at the question, *"Is it necessary to 'identify' and 'guide' the 'gifted' and/or 'superior' children?"* Here we come to the real heart of the problem. It has been shown that each year a large number of high school graduates who have superior intelligence fail to go on to college for one reason or another. The number of such "superior" children is perhaps in the neighborhood of 200,000 per year. Incidentally, if we have identified these children enough to be able to count them, what is all the "identification" talk about?

A serious waste of brain-power is involved and we should try to end it. We should certainly create sufficient scholarships to remove economic barriers from the educational paths of all youngsters. We can no longer look on higher education as a sort of luxury item, which only the more economically favored should receive. We live in a technical society, the very existence of which requires a scientifically and technically educated population. Our society must look on education as both a right and a duty of citizenship and stop considering it a privilege. Our system of universal free education covered only the elementary grades at first. Then it was expanded to cover high schools. Now is the time to extend the program through the college years—for all who can profit from a tough-minded college education.

But what about the "guidance" angle? We should at this point remember the old adage, "You can lead a horse to water but you can't make him drink!" In the past, millions of young people have found their way into science, art, and the humanitarian endeavors without special guidance. Why do today's children need to be guided? It is true that ours is a complex, specialized society, and when it comes to picking out one's specific final occupation, there are lots of choices. But the grade school and high school student doesn't have to face all these choices at once. He need only decide whether he will go to college, and whether he wants to specialize in the general areas of art, or science, or the humanities. Later he can begin to narrow his field of choice within the general area in which he will begin his college courses. If our guidance efforts were organized along these lines, so children would not feel impelled to cross professional bridges before they reach them, the whole problem of guidance would not be made to seem so complicated.

Finally we need to remember that millions of "gifted" and "superior" youngsters have found their way into important careers in science, art and humanitarian fields without being "identified" or "guided" at all. Thinking of this always reminds me of the Columbia River salmon which climb waterfalls and fish ladders beside the dams to reach their goals—the spawning beds in which they were hatched. I can't help feeling that the problem of encouraging children to enter college is not one of "identification" and "guidance." It is rather one of making the goals of achieving fame and fortune sufficiently enticing, and sufficiently realizable, so our youngsters will also be willing to "swim upstream" in order to reach those goals.

The last question, "How accurate must an I.Q. screen be?", is perhaps the most important of all. The answer depends on what kinds of decisions are to be based on the I.Q. score. If you merely want to divide a large group of men into a few broad categories as the Armed Services do in war, the I.Q. tests are quite useful, though even here there are limitations. But if a test given in the grade schools is going to decide whether a child will or will not have the "best" teachers and opportunities in grade school it follows that the child's *whole future development and life* may hinge on the result. With so much at stake, is it not clear that such tests must be close to 100% accurate? As we have seen, intelligence tests simply do not come close to this degree of accuracy. To screen and segregate our children with a test or tests that showed no better than, say, 60% correlation with actual results can lead to nothing good for our children or our society.

Now all of this is not to argue that all children are equally bright; that all children should be in large classes and that all classes should proceed at exactly the same pace. Nor do I feel that we need do nothing to make our schools more interesting and stimulating for our brightest children. There are obvious differences between children— differences in intelligence, energy, motivation, temperament and so on —and these differences need to be taken into account. The basic trouble with intelligence tests is that they ignore too many of these variables and if used to sort out and segregate the "gifted" would seriously weaken the schools for the 95 or 99 percent who are "ungifted."

The most important variable for which there is no test worth mentioning is motivation. It is probably more important for success than any other faculty or quality. The practical effect of segregating children by means of a test or tests is that the "gifted" group will be *given* the very best opportunities, whether their motivations or other qualities are such that they will profit from them or not. The "un-gifted", many of whom may be strongly motivated toward science, and whose possibly lesser natural gifts may need better opportunities more than the "gifted", will be largely shut off from them. The economic barriers to higher education of the past and present have never been as impermeable as these I.Q. segregation barriers, now being advocated, would be.

There are methods of proved worth that can solve these problems without creating new and more serious ones. These are programs which run classes at three or four different speeds. Such programs keep a low enough pupil-to-teacher ratio so good teachers have the time to study their pupils and adjust the individual loads within each section by the use of additional "enrichment" techniques. In this arrangement, the child must win the privilege of running in the fast-speed section by doing superior work *in the subject concerned.* If he finds himself in too fast company, he is permitted to drop back to a slow-paced group. By giving extra assignments to individuals within sections, the teacher then manages to keep the very brightest front runners in all of the different groups from falling into a state of idle boredom. The multi-speed arrangement needs no I.Q. tests. Its decisions are based on a realistic kind of competition which normal children enjoy. Such a system avoids the psychologically and democratically indefensible procedure of segregating the "gifted" from the "ungifted". Finally, it takes cognizance of the fact that most "gifted" children are not "gifted" in all directions. The main tasks of a school system should not be to sort the children in order to turn out a few standardized human Univacs and I.Q. quiz kids. The aim should be to expose all the children to as wide a variety of human activities as possible and to enable every child to find the particular spot in the general scheme which best fits his own skills and aptitudes. The space age we are entering will still need intelligent Indians as well as Chiefs.

Another and most important way of making it possible for children to adjust their own work load to fit their capacities is through the establishment of well supported science clubs. As I will discuss later, every one of our high schools should have a science club with a research laboratory attached to it. Then the fast-learners would have a healthy and useful and educationally sound activity to which they could devote their spare time instead of wasting it in rock-n-roll boredom and delinquency as too many are now doing. Incidentally, I believe the finest W.P.A. project the Federal Government could possibly inaugurate at this time would be one which would facilitate the building of suitable club facilities of this sort for our high schools. Although I am thinking primarily of science, such a program should also be designed to encourage other activities besides science, if investigation indicates a need for them.

That the individual himself is better equipped to find his proper spot than anyone else—including trained counselors—was demonstrated to me very clearly by a World War II experience which occured at the Fort Belvoir, Virginia, training center. Raw recruits were brought there for basic training. A small percentage was found to be "inept." In Army translation, this meant that they had difficulty in quickly doing "right face", "about face", etc. I was assigned to the officer board which screened these soldiers—to eliminate any fakers—before discharging them from the service.

These men were most interesting, for despite the fact that they couldn't react quickly to these Army commands, and so were useless for parades and regimental duties, they were otherwise perfectly normal. Before they were drafted, many of them had held responsible jobs, and I hope they got back to them and weren't too upset after we discharged them. It was quite clear that most of these fellows, despite their "abnormal" reactions to army commands, had never before thought of themselves as "inept." Whatever their peculiarity stemmed from (this would make a good problem for some psychologist to study), they had found their way, *without a psychic usher*, into jobs in which they were useful and productive members of society. It was only when they were placed on the Army treadmill that they became aware of their "ineptness."

In telling this, I am not criticizing the Army. When you have to mobilize, equip and train millions of men you can't stop to fit all the odd-shaped pegs into slots which match them. Crude, relatively inaccurate sorting must be accepted under these emergency circumstances. The I.Q. and other tests were of value in that situation, but the Army also used many other criteria for assigning men, and one of the most important was "common sense." We chided or laughed at the Army's failures but fortunately there was enough "common sense" to make the system work pretty well. I tell the story merely to illustrate how successfully people, even those with handicaps, will find jobs in which they fit, if they have a reasonable opportunity and freedom to pick and choose and change jobs and use *their* "common sense" when they make a mistake or two.

In summary:

(1) All the evidence, when viewed as a whole, shows that intelligence tests are at best only a crude way of classifying people into general categories according to their ability to deal rapidly with the *particular kind of information* contained in the test. Their value as diagnostic tools in research and problem cases is not questioned.

(2) There are many important intellectual qualities such as manual skill and creative imagination, which are not measured at all by I.Q.'s or any other kinds of standard tests.

(3) I.Q. tests completely ignore the factors of motivation which are of the greatest importance for success.

(4) Even though these tests were capable of properly sorting the "gifted", as they are not, their use in the way advocated would ruin our educational system and society by introducing a form of unnatural and illogical segregation into our hitherto free system, and would seriously downgrade the standards of the "ungifted" schools.

(5) The individual himself can usually do the job of finding the spot most suitable for him and do it better than any counsellor or "psychic ushers" we are likely to be able to train.

CHAPTER VI

STICKS AND CARROTS

Prior to the recession that began in 1957, our post war "boom" encouraged the development of a tremendous bureaucratic boondoggle. A great many people had become accustomed to being paid well for producing little or nothing. The disease seems to have been as severe in business as in government. Since most of us have helped to spread the disease, it is not going to be easy to cure and recovery will be painful.

Until Sputnik I, those who pointed to clouds on the economic horizon were accused of being old-fashioned cranks.

Most of us thought—many still do—that the United States was so productive that it could easily support widespread inefficiency and indifference. We could have guns, beer, TV and chrome plate. Didn't we have the strongest economy in the world? Stale themes such as "Just keep up the sales volume and everything will be okay" and "Keep plugging for prosperity" were dinned incessantly in our ears.

We are beginning to see and hear evidence that suggests that "feather-bedding," loafing, carelessness and waste have been insidiously weakening our great productivity. In the investigations of corruption and racketeering in labor and business and even in government, we learned that some of these practices were not small and incidental; they existed on a shockingly large scale.

American science and education have been major victims of this pseudo-prosperity and public indifference and the related inflationary spiral which has so seriously undermined the economic status of many scientists and most teachers; scientists and teachers who have been too poorly organized to protect their economic and professional interests. Ironically, their status has been declining relative to most other professions at the very time the importance of their functions has been growing in the public mind. The generally negative motivation of young people toward science and teaching careers results from their observations of these facts.

The basic cause of our difficulty is that we have gradually transformed a fiercely competitive, capitalist economy into a soft-hearted, soft-headed economic mishmash of a half-socialist, half-capitalist, wel-

46

fare state. This has not been due to alien influences either. Bigness in business, huge government budgets and free spending encouraged a kind of economic complacency that provided a superficially bright facade for a basically unsound situation.

Today there is hardly an area of the economy which is not receiving federal government subsidy in one form or other. Many of the subsidies are outright and direct as, for example, those made to the airline and steamship companies. Subsidies to other businesses **are** often more subtle, but no less real. Protective tariffs, and the results of research and development supported by government and given free to business and agriculture are examples of indirect subsidy. When the government guarantees housing loans on over-priced houses to unsound borrowers, it is "subsidizing" the building industry. When it "adjusts" the margin rates for buying and selling stocks it is protecting the brokerage business. When its Commissions set the interest rates for the banks and profit rates for the railroads and say who can and who can't run a radio or TV station, it is protecting and supporting certain other businesses. Labor receives its government "subsidies" through minimum wage law and through the shifting of defense contracts to areas of unemployment. Probably the most important "subsidies" of labor are those built into labor-management contracts which have the effect in some cases of protecting featherbedding and inefficiency. The price-support "subsidies" to farmers are probably the most widely publicized of all. Of course, each group is against all these "subsidies"—except its own.

I do not intend to criticize or discuss the merits of these actions. I cite them only as examples that prove we no longer have a truly competitive supply and demand economy. Regardless of whatever name you choose to give it, ours is a managed economy. The difficulty so far as science and education are concerned, is in our acting as though we can manage and "subsidize" a large part of the economy and leave the rest "free." The strength that accrues to a business or other activity which has the government committed to support it, places it out of reach of true competition from "free," that is unsubsidized, unsupported, business or other activities. Education and basic science have had that kind of "freedom" and they have been rapidly starving to death.

Now we could not stop these "subsidies" without creating economic chaos. We are more or less in the position of a dope addict. We have a habit, but it can't be stopped suddenly without destroying us. Whether we can ever end most of them is a big economic question that we need not stop to discuss here. One thing I am sure we can do, is to admit the situation frankly and stop deluding ourselves about "our habit." Bring the "subsidies" out in the open. Then the American people can decide, through their representatives, which ones they approve and how much they want to support them. When we compile the list of those to be supported, let us hope education and basic science will be close to the top.

All economies need two opposing motivational forces in order to guide their economic machines effectively. These may be symbolized as "carrots" and "sticks"—rewards and penalties. Both socialism and capitalism require them. The basic differences between these two systems is that socialism emphasizes the "sticks," whereas capitalism emphasizes the "carrots." But neither system works effectively with only one or the other motivational drive. Basic human nature is involved, and there has never been an ecomonic system that can ignore it. In the U.S.S.R. under Stalin, the "sticks" predominated greatly, and while the Soviet economy grew, it showed nothing like the speed and vitality that it has shown since Stalin's death. Khrushchev and company have used "carrots" in a most skillful way. But as Soviet citizens are aware, the "sticks" have not been thrown away. They simply have been placed behind the screen and greater emphasis placed on "carrots."

What has been happening here by comparison? Generally speaking, we have greatly cut down the size and sweetness of our "carrots" and for all practical purposes we have thrown the "sticks" away. The possibility of getting rich through personal effort, ingenuity or enterprise has grown so remote that few are making the effort. Instead of working, one makes contacts. The high tax rates and inflation have made it virtually impossible for anyone, even people with high incomes, to save substantial amounts of capital. The individual who "strikes it rich" by writing a successful novel, or patenting a new invention, or becoming an entertainment star has most of his financial rewards confiscated by taxation. So the prevailing attitude is, "What's the use?"

So much for "carrots." The biggest and sweetest ones are certainly being given to the managers and servants of industry and government. The day of big "carrots" for the successful inventor or prospector or small operator is gone. What about our "sticks?" The two major "sticks" in the past have been the threat of unemployment and of poverty in old age. For nearly twenty years before the 1957 recession began there had been no serious unemployment. No one under thirty-five years of age and few above it worried about having a job. Few saved for a "rainy day." "Rainy days" were supposed to have been banished, and the finance companies were doing all the saving.

Through federal and private unemployment insurance, through seniority rights enforced by union contracts, through the government policy of shifting defense contracts to areas of unemployment, workers had been led to believe that prolonged unemployment is impossible. Their attitude was something like this, "The government won't let a depression with wide-scale unemployment occur because to do so would lead to socialism." Beneath the attitude was the threat, "We'll fix those politicians and bureaucrats if they allow that to happen to us."

Even the threat of poverty in old age is no longer a strong motivating force for most people. Between social security and private pension schemes, most individuals in business and government expect to have adequate retirement incomes. Few of them fully realize that inflation could reduce the buying power of this anticipated income to a fraction of its present value. Also "getting ahead" has not been so easy for other reasons. In many situations, seniority is the most important factor in getting ahead. Where seniority is not absolute, there are many ways the group uses to keep the "eager beavers" from being too eager and trying too hard to get ahead. These practices are by no means restricted to union "groups." So the goal has been switched from "get ahead" to "get along" and the net effect is the massive social inertia of togetherness, other-directedness and group-think. The pioneer type who opened up and developed this continent finds himself out of step.

All these recent social changes in the relative values of our "sticks" and "carrots" have affected science and education just as they have business. How have they done so? In the first place the financial rewards in the post-war economy have not been such as to encourage youngsters to take hard courses like mathematics and science in order to have careers in engineering and medicine. The easier courses in personality development and social adjustment and advertising psychology were the paths to salesmanship and management—careers where the best salaries are. The choices of youngsters are conditioned by the value scale their elders have placed before their eyes. Now we are bemoaning the attitudes of youngsters and do not see that they are merely a reflection of our own. Warren Weaver, vice-president of the Rockefeller Foundation has described the attitude of

the general public in these words " . . . . many would treat scientists
one-third of the time as amusing but beneficial eccentrics, one-third
of the time as sorcerers, and one-third of the time as irresponsible
rascals." Can we expect or hope that our children will be attracted
to such an image?

Let us turn our attention to the actual work-life of adults whose
careers are in education and science—teachers and scientists. The
financial rewards of working in areas of science not related to defense
"hardware" have, like those of teachers, also been declining relatively.
Of course, to a large degree basic scientists and college science teachers
are the same people. At the same time that their "carrots" have
grown less juicy, the menacing "sticks" have been much in evidence.
Scientists and teachers have been made the whipping boy of our day.

Until the Sputniks, our leaders explained every Soviet scientific
achievement not on their own bad organization and management, but
as due to "security leaks" by egghead scientists. It was a great system while it lasted, "heads the bureaucrats won, tails the scientists
lost." This is why many of the best brains in our country are not
working in defense industries or for government. Until we completely
end this shell game, we cannot expect to get the maximum from our
scientific brains.

In universities, foundations and scientific organizations the top
salaries go to the administrators and managers. In general, the rewards for basic science workers have declined by comparison. Only
in areas of science related to the making of "hardware," areas where
there is a relative shortage, have the financial rewards remained reasonably good. But in general the basic scientist, whose only product
is ideas—ideas which are generally of such a nature that they can not
possibly be patented—must as always continue to give them away,
and for relatively less salary than formerly. Even in the realms of
kudos, American scientists get short-changed. Consider the reci-
pients of honorary degrees each June. How many among them are
honored for scientific work? Unfortunately, the American public
generally knows little about our important scientists, unless they receive a European prize, are refused a passport, or are "odd-balls" the
newspapers play up with subtle derision.

Let us consider what kind of kudos some of our top scientists have
received in the past. Readers who are older than 35 or 40 will remember the way Einstein was made the butt of numerous sly jokes
in the papers and elsewhere. Because he was a simple man who
slouched about the Princeton campus in a turtle-neck sweater, let

his hair grow long and ate ice-cream cones in public, he made good "copy." Newspaper writers and photographers failed to realize that this one-sided, slightly ridiculous portrayal of one of the world's greatest scientists damaged the prestige of all scientists.

A month before Linus Pauling was named for the 1954 Nobel prize in chemistry, he had been denied a full passport and according to the New York Times was offered "a strictly limited passport that would not let him keep his engagements." Since receiving the Nobel Prize, he has had no more passport difficulties.

Our world-famous Nobel prize geneticist, H. J. Muller, was embarrassed by having the U.S. Program Committee remove his paper at the last minute from the program of the Geneva "Atoms for Peace" Conference because he had commented on the effects of radiation on survivors of Hiroshima and Nagaski. A loud reaction from scientists all over the world was immediately heard, and the State Department fumbled for two or three days trying to "explain" its action. During the actual conference, Dr. Muller's name was mentioned as he sat in the gallery. He received a standing ovation from the assembled group, which was not only a tribute to him but also an embarrassing rebuke to our government.

Dr. Edward U. Condon, former director of the National Bureau of Standards, has described the "rewards" he received for making outstanding contributions to the A-bombs, the H-bombs and more recently to the design of nose-cones which can be recovered from rockets fired into outer space. Dr. Condon described his experience as follows:

" [Over the past ten years] I have had two full-scale loyalty hearings in the Department of Commerce, a full-field investigation for the Atomic Energy Commission, and finally in 1954 had a hearing under the policies and procedures set up by this Administration. In all of these I received full clearance. All covered essentially the same ground which was no ground at all . . . .

"During most of this period I kept on working to develop the scientific strength and stature of the National Bureau of Standards. . . .

"Edward Teller told this last personnel security board hearing in April, 1954 that the Bureau's work on the hydrogen bomb which I organized advanced our achievement of that goal by many months, probably a year. If he is correct in the implication that without that work we would have been delayed by about a year, then the lack of that work would have made us come in second in the international rivalry for the hydrogen bomb.

"Nevertheless all the old stuff was rehashed once in 1952 and again in 1954. I was badgered all those years for having been interested in the American-Soviet Science Society, an organization which received a grant from the Rockefeller Foundation ten years ago to foster translation and wider distribution in this country of the Russian scientific literature. Now, a decade later we read of crash programs to translate the Russian scientific literature and spread it around in this country. Why, man, you can't do that; that's subversive.

"In July, 1954 I was given complete security clearance by the Eastern Industrial Personnel Security Board. You might think now that I would be allowed to go back to work. Yet, in Oct. 1954, just before the elections . . . I was arbitrarily suspended without any pretense that additional evidence needed to be considered. . . .

"Try to picture the situation. I had been under steady political attack for seven years, and had won at every hearing. But now I was told that I would have to go over all the same material again, before a kangaroo court whose members were to be handpicked to do their job by Defense Department officials . . . .

"Under these circumstances . . . I decided the situation was hopeless, and that I had done all that could reasonably be expected of me in having resisted these evil, dishonorable forces for seven long years.

"In those seven years so much of my nervous energy had gone into the struggle that I was weary unto sickness, and was forced to neglect the proper courtship of our beloved profession. So I decided to withdraw from the struggle, and my resignation from an industrial position for which security clearance was needed was announced in early December.

"You might think that now I would be allowed to go back to work. I came East in January 1955 after giving my retiring presidential address to the American Association for the Advancement of Science and was offered the post of chairman of the department of physics in a leading university. In March the chancellor of that university told me that he could not follow through on the appointment because a high government official threatened one of the university trustees that if my appointment went through, that university would lose all of its Federal funds.

"In June of 1955 I was asked to serve on a committee on a nonclassified problem of military importance—and then suddenly asked not to, just before the first meeting of that committee.

"Incidentally I was cleared from July 1954 to October 1954. During that period some Navy people came to see me with an urgent problem on the development of a radome for a guided missile. It was highly secret, but I was cleared for it. By the time we had the development models made my clearance had been suspended, 'pending further consideration.' "

The public has been led to believe that our scientists are not really interested in practical things. Scientists in this fairy tale are portrayed as "dedicated" people who are not concerned with and who scarcely understand money matters. This is sheer nonsense. Our scientists like all people not only enjoy being honored for their work, they also enjoy the comforts of living. They require money! Unless we can find a way to pay our scientists both money and kudos comparable to those we give businessmen, lawyers, doctors, and others, we cannot hope to keep our science team in the "big leagues." Even though the "fun" of discovering and communicating new ideas is an important motivating force in science, it will not be adequate to solve our recruitment problem unless the money "carrots" for basic science are greatly improved.

Besides greatly increasing the money rewards for scientists and teachers a real system of awarding kudoes for successful scientific achievement must be established. In order to give leadership in this, Congress should establish a National Hall of Fame for Scientists, Educators and others who have made major contributions toward the advancement of knowledge and human welfare. We already have Halls of Fame for baseball and football players. The baseball and football promoters started them because they wanted to attract the interest of young people and fans to their sports. They had the money to take such a step. Science, as such, is a pauper. If it is to have a Hall of Fame, Congress will have to pay for it.

And while Congress is doing that it should also establish a series of prizes equivalent to the Nobel Peace Prizes. Awards should be given each year for outstanding work performed in science or education in the preceding five or perhaps ten years. When this is done we should bestow the first set of prizes upon those dedicated individuals who have "held the line" for science and education in the recent past. Two people of the type I have in mind have been public educators in the broadest sense—even though they were not attached to educational institutions.

Miss Margaret E. Patterson has been executive director of Science Clubs of America since its formation in 1942. She has been the catalytic agent in encouraging and promoting the formation of thousands of high school science clubs since then. Had it not been for the interest in science and encouragement toward science careers which these clubs have induced in thousands of youngsters, America would probably be in a second rate position at this time, though, of course, we would be able to console ourselves that we still were "tops" in baseball and football.

A second individual who has done very much to teach American adults the value and meaning of basic science, and to demonstrate to all of us the way todays' basic science becomes tomorrows medical practice, is Basil O'Connor, the head of the National Foundation for Infantile Paralysis.

People such as these, who had the wisdom and courage and enthusiasm and ability to "sell" science when there was little public or official interest, deserve to be rewarded. No doubt there are many other educators who deserve such recognition, and of course there are first rate American scientists whose work should also be suitably recognized by prizes. A few who come quickly to mind are the late Dr. Evarts Graham, the man who pioneered modern chest surgery, and Dr. Alfred Blalock, who pioneered heart surgery. Thousands are living normal lives today, who would be dead if it were not for the work of these men and their associates. There are many many more outstanding American scientists and educators. We need to "identify" them and honor them. Incidentally, we might even name a few streets after them and erect a few statues as they do in Europe. The youngsters will notice that and they'll get the idea that science as well as baseball and football are important.

When we consider the utterly ridiculous fashion in which scientists have fared on this "sticks" and "carrots" scale, is it any wonder that our children are not looking for exciting scientific careers, but rather for safe, soft, business careers; that they prefer the easy social studies leading to cushy management jobs to the hard science studies leading to the basic research laboratories and school teaching. The hard studies quite obviously lead to a hard life, whereas the soft ones lead to a soft life. Could any choice have been made simpler for them?

CHAPTER VII

ENCOURAGING AND STIMULATING CURIOSITY

From what you read in the papers and the magazines you might conclude that the problem of getting scientists is something like catching mice in a trap. You set a trap, bait it with a little cheese, and wait. You assume that the mice are not as smart as you are. You often catch a mouse that way. The trouble is that the mice you catch by this technique are the stupid ones. The really smart and sensitive and "mature" ones detect the human scent of your fingers mingled with the cheese, and they wisely by-pass the whole situation, ignore your cheese and keep up their high standard of living at your expense. Fortunately for the future of micekind, there have always been enough smart mice to insure the survival of the species. From the point of view of mice, I'm sure you'll agree, this is very important.

Since up to the present time no one has suggested anything much more substantial to attract young people to science than to put a little scholarship "cheese" on the trap, we must consider the psychology of young people in order to defend them from the assumption that they are no brighter than the stupid mice.

We are now being told that the nation which is able to get the largest number of bright "mice" to make weapons for it may be able to dominate those nations which don't have quite so many or quite such bright "mice." This creates a new situation, for over the past few years we have often been hitting our bright "mice" over the head and declaring them to be "security risks." Is it surprising now that the young bright "mice" are taking a close look at the whole situation before they nibble the enticements being offered them to become scientists? This situation clearly puts a certain "veto" power in their hands.

Isn't it time we accepted the fact that we cannot urge young people to become scientists, unless we are willing to promise them we will reward them for their later efforts so long as they are scientifically honest; promise them we will not punish them at some future date if they follow our current advice and go into science. If we accept this proposition, we must solemnly promise ourselves and them

55

that we will give them a fair share of financial rewards; and that ten or twenty or thirty years from now if some future McCarthy tries to pillory them as "eggheads," or "bleeding hearts" or "communists" (perhaps because they believe in the evolutionary theory or desegregation or free speech), we will spring to their defense. Only on the basis of that promise are we in a morally defensible position to examine the operational question: "How do you get more scientists?"

First, let us define what a scientist is. In administrative terms, a scientists is a man or woman with a doctor's degree or at least a master's degree in some branch of science. But to get a master's or doctor's degree, one must usually get a bachelor's degree and this means getting a high school diploma and before that a grade school diploma.

But you may say, "Is that all there is to it? I know lots of people who have master's and doctor's degrees who are not scientists." You've hit on the heart of the matter. Being a scientist is, of course, not only a matter of education. In fact, to be a scientist does not necessarily require a formal education at all. Because of the great interest in applied science—medicine and engineering—our schools today overemphasize scientific facts and techniques. These are what the students are usually tested on rather than on the ability to think. Too many young people seem to be preparing to win TV quizzes and too few to think. The essence of science derives not from technical school credentials but from a point of view and from the development of imagination. Creative scientists are basically people who have cultivated their skepticism and their imagination in order to create new ideas. They are people whose most beloved credo has been eloquently and beautifully stated in the song, " 'Tain't necessarily so." Even when he is presenting his latest theory, the true scientist has his fingers crossed and is saying softly, " 'Tain't necessarily (entirely) so!" or at least " 'Tain't necessarily all I'd like to know!" The point of view is probably not one that originates in college or high school or even in grade school. Of course, it can be encouraged in schools, but its real origin and development depends on encouragement to think independently and stimulation to think imaginatively in the very early pre-school period. Creative theories are the mature equivalents of childhood fantasies.

The importance of the pre-school fantasies cannot be proved in the sense that physical facts can. But there is considerable evidence which supports the belief that the child's imagination should be encouraged and not repressed. My own childhood experience convinces me about this point. Of course, to a large extent my ideas about motivation are derived from personal experience—and where else, but inwardly, can anyone turn to check the validity of theories about motivation? In recent years, when I have heard so much frantic discussion about the need to stimulate more children to enter science, I have asked myself "Why did I become a scientist?" Thinking back to my early childhood it seems to me that the key factors were in my mother's ideas about education. She had great respect for the power and pleasure and value of knowledge. She believed that babies and infants and children were intelligent human beings whose questions deserved to be answered with as much honesty and respect as those of adults. She also believed that children's minds needed to be stimulated, needed to be encouraged to unfold. By answering a child's question carefully you encourage him to think some more and ask further questions, and so on and on. Because of these beliefs my mother provided us, and many of her friends' children as well, with books and toys which she hoped would produce this stimulation. By studying the pictures in the "Book of Life" and asking questions about them, I had learned, even before entering kindergarten, a great many facts about the stars, the planets, the earth and its inhabitants. By then, too, I had discovered the fascination of magnification.

I was given a simple instrument constructed so that bugs or caterpillars could be placed and held in its forward chamber, to be viewed in magnified size through the eyepiece. According to my mother, I used to spend hours observing enlarged bugs and worms. Thus, before I went to school at all, I had begun to study the two major "mysteries": What is life? Who made the earth and me? One is the question that looks inward toward the very small, the atom, the other looks outward toward the infinite universe. Man's size which, in terms of magnitudes, is about midway between the size of atoms and the size of the universe, is ideal for looking both ways. All other science questions are encompossed in these two questions. I am still interested in the same questions and scientifically studying the first one. I now ask, "What is the bio-chemical explanation of aging?" Perhaps this is a little more sophisticated, but the question is essentially unchanged. And, of course, astronomers are studying the second question, "Who Made the Earth and Me?" They phrase it: "How did the universe originate?"

Because of my own early experience and the large amount of

supporting evidence in the literature of psychology and education indicating the importance of pre-school years for subsequent development, I believe that the best way to get more scientists is not
to place our primary emphasis on luring high school graduates into
science because we want them to create rockets and gadgets, but
rather to develop pre-school programs to encourage the natural
curiosity and imagination of those babies and young children from
homes with low intellectual standards. Children so encouraged will
later go into science and other intellectual pursuits *because they
want to* and not because *we* want them to. Unfortunately, only a
small minority of American children are receiving the kind of intellectual encouragement and stimulation I have described. Thousands of our children never see a book before they enter school.
Certainly the number who are privileged to look through a magnifying
glass, microscope or telescope before they enter school is still smaller.

I am certain the most important long range step we can take to
increase the number of good scientists in the future will be to establish enough nursery schools to provide this kind of opportunity for
all children whose homes do not provide it for them. If all the
children from such homes could spend at least three or four, prefer-
ably more, hours a day during the pre-school period in a good nursery school or kindergarten where they would receive stimulation and
encouragement to develop their minds, we would not have to write
so many science recruitment pamphlets.

In this country most of the approximately 1¼ million children
who now attend nursery schools and kindergartens are the children
of parents able to encourage and guide them in intellectual directions. Probably among such children the interest in scientific matters
would develop just about as often whether or not they attended
nursery school. But if we were to extend this pre-school opportunity
to all our children, especially to those who come from intellectually
under-privileged homes, we would encourage a large *new* group to
raise their educational goals.

I have discussed this proposal with a number of our top psychologists. They agree that the pre-school years are undoubtedly of
fundamental importance in directing the intellectual interests and
goals which children later pursue and that more nursery schools would
probably be effective in stimulating more children to be interested
in science. As I have said, there is a great deal of evidence in both
educational and psychological literature which strongly supports this
thesis. What stands in the way of our doing something like this?

One hurdle to overcome is the fact that our leaders are interested mainly in "crash" programs—programs which will produce an I.C.B.M. and also help its political sponsors win the next election. Of course, a program directed at stimulating children from ages three to seven to become interested in the secrets of nature won't "pay-off" for twenty or more years. "Practical" politicians and industrialists are not generally thinking about such long range projects.

A second barrier to be surmounted is our lack of understanding of the importance of the early years in setting future intellectual goals. We ignore the fact that when we leave the matter of stimulating and guiding children's thoughts entirely to chance, we are leaving it to the advertising agencies whose main interest is in developing customers for their products. Today our children, especially those raised in culturally-backward homes, get most of their early knowledge of the outside-the-family world from the TV programs of the breakfast food and other industries.

Let us look at some of the evidence relative to the nursery school proposal. Studies show that I.Q. scores can be increased by stimulation or relatively decreased by its absence. Children whose I.Q. scores were at the "feeble minded" level actually have raised their scores to normal levels when placed in foster homes with families of normal intelligence. In the previous chapter it was pointed out that nursery school stimulation given to half the children in an orphanage improved the average I.Q. of the group which received it as compared with the group which did not.

For over a generation, the Soviet educational system has recognized the importance of this kind of experimental data. They have developed a tremendous program of pre-school education. At latest report, over 5 million children were attending their nursery schools and kindergartens. Through the use of education in these early years they have actually learned how to by-pass the cultural backwardness of former generations. It seems likely that the widespread interest of Soviet children in science careers has its beginning in these pre-school activities. It is important in considering this matter to realize that the 5 million or more Soviet children attending these pre-schools are to a large extent the children of parents of generally limited intellectual backgrounds. These parents would be poorly equipped to provide the equivalent of pre-school stimulation even if they were not working and were free to do so. In contrast the 1¼ million American pre-school youngsters who attend nursery schools and kindergartens usually have parents of superior intellectual attainments. Most of the American children would be encouraged in intellectual directions even if they did not go to nursery school or kindergarten.

This Soviet emphasis on pre-school education is one of the most striking differences between our educational systems. If this early stimulation of children, many of whose own parents could not provide it, is the key to their large number of science graduates today, there is no "crash" program we can counter with. We can only find our own ways of giving our children the equivalent of what they give theirs. We must face the fact that *we can't compete with Soviet science if we can't find an American way of doing for our children what the Soviets are doing for theirs*. We have heard that we are several years behind the Soviets in the missiles race, but that we can catch up with a "crash" program. If the pre-school program is as important as I believe it is no "crash" program can close the gap.

CHAPTER VIII

PAY, PRESTIGE, AND SCIENCE TEACHING

Everyone agrees that we must have more and better trained scientists in this country. Public statements on how to get this result focus on the need for developing a larger corps of well-qualified fulltime science teachers in our secondary schools. This emphasis is a block to the solution of our science training, for it narrows the attack too greatly. Our strategy is to produce scientists. The tactics for achieving this goal are numerous and getting more and better science teachers is only one approach.

There are thousands of first-rate, dedicated, underpaid science teachers who are doing an outstanding job against tremendous odds. But there are not enough of them to counteract the vicious cycle that results from those inadequate science teachers who create in children and their parents an attitude of indifference or even dislike of science. This contributes to a lack of general public interest and appreciation of science. Without public support, we cannot get the tax support needed to improve the status of science teaching. The result comes back full circle to inadequate science teaching. The basic fault, however, is not with the teachers, but with ourselves.

How can we break this cycle? General David Sarnoff of the Radio Corporation of America has suggested a new and revolutionary approach to this problem. He pointed out that we have a large body of well trained physicists, chemists, biologists, engineers and physicians. Only a few of them now teach in our universities and colleges. Almost none of them teach in our high schools. General Sarnoff suggested that these scientists temporarily take over part of the high school science teaching job. The suggestion is a good one, but I think the arrangement should be a permanent one. Before giving a few of the organizational details of how this could be done, let me explain briefly why I feel this is probably the only way we can solve this problem.

To be a good teacher of science today requires a good science education. The theory of some educationists that all one needs in order to teach any subject is a knowledge of teaching techniques is nonsense. Teaching basic science to bright, interested students requires that one have a vast store of well organized facts and theory *in his head,* not in some books on the shelf.

But why should a well trained young scientist teach science in a high school for low pay; teach in a school environment which provides none of the pleasures, excitement and stimulation of research; teach and live in a community environment where his prestige is low? Why should he teach in a secondary school when he can have more pay, better research opportunities and higher prestige working in industry, government, or in a university or private research institution? There are no sensible affirmative answers to these questions and that is why so few youngsters are entering the science teaching field today.

A survey of 199 communities in New York state reported in *Time* magazine of October 15, 1956, revealed these attitudes: "Four out of ten children and nearly half the parents polled said they have no respect for their teachers' knowledge. Only 24% of the adults said they admire teachers. In 79 communities, more than half the male teachers hold down after-hours jobs to make ends meet. Most communities (74%) take it for granted that teachers should perform after-school duties with no extra pay. Only 18% of the parents said they would like to see their sons go into teaching, but an almost equal number said 'Absolutely not.' "

Because such adverse attitudes of young people toward teaching careers have only become a cause of national concern in the post-Sputnik era, we have not yet fully plumbed the psychology which accounts for them. In addition to the obvious deficiencies in pay, enjoyment, and prestige, there is an important negative factor which has been overlooked. This has been the present widespread belief in the "guaranteed job."

In the pre-war period, teaching possessed one major advantage over an industrial job. It was safe and sure and more or less "depression proof." True, the prospects for advancement were limited, but there was much to be said for a job which was reasonably safe from economic threats even though the rewards were not so big as in other less secure fields. But, in a country where the "stick" of unemployment had not, until the latter part of 1957, been felt for nearly twenty years, those who were less than 35 years of age scarcely believe it ever existed. To most young people and even to a good many of those older than 35 the "stick" is absent from their planning.

This attitude was clearly shown in a study of 1955 Lehigh college graduates. Here are the factors these seniors considered most important in choosing a job: 1: Interesting work. 2: Good training programs. 3: Opportunities for advancement. 4: Salaries equal to others in field. 5: Retirement security. 6: Location for good living conditions.

Not a word to suggest that they thought anything of job security— just "Where is the best pasture?" Job security is assumed. Now we obviously cannot look to unemployment as a means of restoring the "stick" to our economic system and. thus providing a negative encouragement for youngsters to go into teaching.

But when I compare teaching to such careers as applied science and to business administration on the "carrot" scale of the Lehigh seniors, it seems to me it is impossible for high school teaching to attract enough young people to solve our science teaching problem. There is just too big a differential in favor of the job in applied science or business administration, *working for industry or government* or doing research in other institutions. Therefore, the only approach that seems feasible is for universities, research institutes, industry and government to assume *full* responsibility for staffing our high school science classes. Let them hire *all* young science graduates and then "farm" them out to the schools to teach for a part of their careers— a sort of science interneship program. The local schools would reimburse the companies and/or government agencies for this service on a contractual basis so it would not be an expense of these organizations.

A reorganization of this kind could be worked out largely at local levels. The high schools and some small colleges that might choose to join such a plan know what teaching services they want. Most high schools are situated close enough to sources of practicing scientists to be able to follow this proposal. If there are isolated schools where such a proposal cannot be implemented, other arrangements could be worked out.

Industry, government and other local institutions which employ scientists could unite to perform this Community Teaching Service by organizing a jointly managed teaching corporation. This organization would then be able to contract with the local education authorities to provide this educational service.

There are many legal and administrative precedents for this kind of jointly managed organization. Companies have often formed such corporations to handle problems too large for any one of them to handle alone or to provide non-competitive services which all of them need.

Such an arrangement should absorb all the existing full-time science teachers into the teaching corporation. And it should protect their pension and other rights as well. No doubt many of these teachers would be helped by this arrangement to improve and update their knowledge. Those teachers trained in deficient educational systems during the past 20 or so years should not be made the scape-goats of the present situation. Those who have been the victims of the educationist system should be given special help to improve their knowledge and teaching skills.

This arrangement will also have an extremely important extra-dividend. By bringing scientists from the local community back into the schools, we will reestablish a bridge between science and society. This bridge is badly needed to end the unnatural estrangement between science and society that has developed in the past fifty years or so—the very years during which we have become a great scientifically based, industrial nation. No doubt our emphasis on the practical, technical aspects of science, almost to the exclusion of basic science has made it possible to achieve this industrial development. But now we need to emphasize basic science as much as we have emphasized applied science.

We must restore science to the "grass roots" where it began. In order to encourage the interest of both children and adults in science, I propose that we establish research laboratories separate from the teaching laboratories in our high schools and small colleges. It is not true that in order to do research it is necessary to have thousands of dollars worth of elaborate equipment. All you need is one good question. The 1957 Nobel prizes in medicine were given to three doctors for developing and perfecting the technique of cardiac catheterization. The original basic experiment in this series was performed by a German physician, Dr. Werner Forssmann, who passed a rubber tube costing no more than a few dollars through a vein into his own heart. The 1950 Nobel prize in physics was won by British physicist, C. F. Powell whose experiment required only photographic plates exposed to cosmic rays high on an Andean mountain, and a microscope. Some of the fundamental research on the physical properties of rubber was performed by Dr. Milton L. Braun at little Catawba (South Carolina) College, whose research required a ruler, some weights, a thermometer and a box of rubber bands. In each of these experiments, the penetrating question and not the equipment was the significant factor.

Establishing local research laboratories in which youngsters will work and which their parents will see and understand is the only way to restore lasting public interest in and understanding of science.

Good TV programs about science are fine, but they are no substitute for personal participation. You can no more get the maximum mental excercise as a science spectator than you can get physical exercise by watching a baseball game. Of course I do not mean that *every* child would take a course in research. But the teachers should have the facilities and time and encouragement to do part-time research. There will be bright students who will join them on a voluntary basis.

That children are interested in such matters and some of them capable of doing work that would do credit to adults has been demonstrated by the experience of Science Clubs of America. Today there are over 17,000 affiliated clubs with over ⅓ of a million boys and girls working in them. The size of the clubs varies from 3 to 700 members. Most of these have been organized on a "boot-strap" basis since 1942.

In considering this question of "grass roots" research it is of great interest to contrast the facilities we provide our children with those the Soviets are providing for such experience.

The 1958 Science Club "Sponsors Handbook" (available from Science Service, 1719 "N" Street, N.W., Wash., D.C.) has this to say on "Where Can Our Club Meet?": "The popular headquarters for science clubs are in school laboratories. In many cities this is the most concentrated collection of scientific apparatus available. See if you can get permission to use it.

"Investigate basement, attic and old building laboratories. Many amateurs have elaborate set-ups which can be used for small groups of students. A person with an extensive private photographic laboratory may be willing to sponsor a small photographic club for beginners. A shop foreman may have his own basement shop that will provide working space and equipment for a group wishing to do wood or metal work. Situations like these are common in every city and may be more satisfactory than the school 'lab' which may be closed or already reserved for nights.

"Look around for any college or university accommodations that can be used. Is there a museum with educational facilities? Is there an industrial plant that can spare space for training groups?

"There is always the out-of-doors. This is the 'lab' for groups doing nature study, gardening, conservation, plane flying, etc.

"A club may start with practically nothing and assemble its own laboratory and club equipment by donations; building and buying apparatus as it can afford it."

The 1957 publication of the Department of Health, Education and

Welfare on "Education in the U.S.S.R." says this about activities organized outside the Soviet school:

"The largest variety of extracurricular programs is organized at establishments created primarily to provide activities for the out-of-school time of children. These activities are under Communist Party and trade union auspices. The Party establishments, called 'Pioneer Palaces' and 'Pioneer Houses,' are duplicated to a large extent in clubs, known as Palaces and Houses of Culture, which are maintained by trade unions. At such clubs, which are integrated with the school curriculum, members and their families may engage in the same kinds of extracurricular activities as those [clubs] available in the schools."

"Facilities of the Pioneer Palaces in Leningrad, Tashkent, Alma-Ata, Ashkabad, Tbilisi, and many other cities are reportedly extensive. The one in Leningrad, for example, formerly was an imperial palace. It is one of the largest and most elaborate in the country with a library and provisions for activities in technology, science, art, sports, and political work. Its technology division, for example, claims: (1) An aviation engineering section with shops for work in aerodynamics, motors and engines for aircraft, model airplanes, and gliders; (2) a transportation section with workship facilities for learning about motors, railroads, ship building, and city electric transport systems; (3) a photography motion-picture section with laboratories and dark-rooms; (4) a communications section with rooms set aside for work with radio, telephone, and telegraph equipment; (5) an electrical power section with 5 laboratories; (6) a mechanics section; (7) a graphics section; (8) a carpentry-mechanics section; (9) a mechanics section; (10) a laboratory for work with house painting techniques; (11) a machine assembly laboratory; and (12) a machine construction section."

The suggested Community Teaching Service plan, especially if the local research laboratories were also established as a part of the program, would no doubt be welcome to many of the applied scientists who would be involved. The arrangement would take them back into basic research as well as give them some teaching experience. I am sure both of these opportunities would be welcomed by most scientists. Naturally, the research done in these school laboratories would be exclusively basic research. So, we would have an extra dividend—more basic research by a group whose jobs have not allowed them to do basic research, aided and assisted by thousands of eager youngsters.

Under this arrangement the schools would get a better grade of science teacher than they can now attract and the scientists would get the experience of teaching and doing basic research which many now miss. Teaching is itself the best teacher. The experience generally deepens the teacher's knowledge of humanity as well as of subject matter. Higher education, research institutes, industry and government would all benefit from this program. They would have a "seasoning" plant where their people would grow keen in their science internships by sharpening themselves on the fine stone of classroom teaching.

High school students would be learning science from those who believed in it enough to choose it as a career. Such teachers should surely be more enthusiastic "salesmen" for science than the usually underpaid, often poorly prepared and sometimes reluctant science teachers staffing many of the high school science departments at present. There can be no doubt that through the Community Teaching Service, science would achieve important status in its competition for the best young minds.

Science does have certain non-monetary "rewards"—the enjoyment of which many commercial and industrial jobs lack. But this enjoyment can best be described to young people by scientists who have experienced it or better still by the students themselves experiencing it in actual work in a research laboratory.

One final advantage of these proposals is that they would bring more men into the teaching profession. Some studies indicate that the higher standards of education and the lower rates of delinquency in Europe are related to the stronger role men play both in school and home life. If this is true, we shall, in making this change, not only have better educated young scientists, but better disciplined young people as well.

CHAPTER IX

ON CHOOSING AND TENDING "HORSES"

In the post-Sputnik era there are demands on all sides for more basic research. Even the general public has suddenly become aware of and concerned about basic research, though it still is asking what it is. Of course, this interest stems from the fact that Soviet basic research got a satellite into outer space before we did. Our competitive instincts were instantly aroused.

We are accustomed to buying anything we want, so we now talk as though more money is all that's needed to get more basic research. But is more money all that is needed? The fact is, that unless we change our administrative system for supporting basic research, putting up more money for it actually may get less, not more.

Such a statement naturally provokes interest in the present "system." But, an understanding of how the "system" works will show why this is so. I place quotations around the word system because the word usually implies more central coordination and planning than actually exists. Since American science has not one but many "heads," it really has none. It is a loose federation of a number of competing systems.

How does this "system" work? The dominant way of supporting all research in the United States, basic as well as developmental, has been to support *projects*. "Grants-in-aid" are made for conducting specific projects. Applications for such "grants-in-aid" describe a specific project, tell why the investigator considers it worthy of support, and present a fairly detailed budget of the funds needed to carry out the project. The alternative way of supporting basic research, which has repeatedly proved its effectiveness in other countries since the time of the Italian Renaissance, is to support people and institutions.

Dr. Curt Richter, well-known Johns Hopkins physiologist, has urged that we "support the man" instead of projects. Writing in *Science*, he described the present committee decisions on projects this way: "In most instances all we know about a project is what we see written on a piece of paper—the application blank—words. We do not know the man, we may never have heard of him.

68

This means that in most instances we must vote the way we bet on horses at the races, because we like the name, the number or the stable." Of course professional gamblers don't bet on mere hunches. They study the horses, the weather, the tracks, the jockeys, and many other factors before they place their bets. But Dr. Richter is entirely right in comparing our method of "betting" on basic research projects to the amateur gambler's method of betting on horse races.

The need for changing this policy has been expressed by other prominent educators and scientists. One of them, Dr. James B. Conant, former Harvard president, has said, "Don't appraise the project, but the proposed investigator; don't bet on the subject, but on the man." Another of our famous scientists, Dr. Paul Weiss of the Rockefeller Institute has said this: "The well-channeled roads of mass traffic are also the ways of least effort and resistance, offering the security that lies in numbers, and the comfort that comes with conformance. To travel them does not call for the vision and daring and fanatical devotion of the pioneer. Procedures are neatly mapped out, equipment ready-made, and tangible results are the more certainly assured, the more narrowly circumscribed the task. . . . The risk is small, the reward assured. And this, of course, appeals to those who crave security. Coincidentally, our prevailing system of research support by project grants plays into their hands and confirms them in their attitude."

Dr. Detlev Bronk, President of the Rockefeller Foundation and of the American Academy of Science, has said this on the subject: "Many of the most important discoveries of scientific research have come from the intellectual adventures of individual scientists. . . . . Many scientific discoveries will continue to elude direction and organization as surely as would the creation of great music or poetry, or sculpture or art. Much of scientific research is exploration of the unknown, and I, for one, do not believe it is possible to direct the course of an explorer through unexplored territory."

In the face of such criticism from important scientists and administrators, why do we continue the project system for supporting basic research? The answer probably stems from the fact that in this country most of our earliest support was for applied or developmental research—specific projects. In those early days we made no effort to distinguish between applied and basic work. The total programs were small. No one was much concerned and both types of research were handled under a single program. Probably inertia, more than anything else, keeps us from changing now. Of course, the project system

works for developing new weapons, new technical improvements in
agriculture, medicine and so on. But it is not a good way to support
basic research. Money-wise, projects for applied research will no
doubt always be a much larger budget item than that for basic research. But that doesn't mean that the two types of research must
be lumped together and administered in the same way.

We probably need not abandon project support for pursuing goals,
which have been clearly identified, and when we know approximately *how to reach them*. This kind of research should be done for the
most part by private laboratories, and it should be done on a sound
business basis, in which the contractor and contractee deal with
each other just as other buyers and sellers do. It should not be done
by Universities or other educational institutions. Their job is the
advancement of basic knowledge, not the exploitation of it.

But as Dr. Bronk said, basic research is concerned with explorations unto *unknown territory* and so it is asking the impossible when
we request a basic researcher to provide exploratory maps into this
unknown unexplored territory. Although the truth of this statement
is obvious we are still going through the motions of doing just that
when we use the project system for making basic research grants.
As a practical matter most agencies actually permit the investigators
the greatest latitude in modifying their projects *as they wish* after
the projects have been approved and grants made. If it were not
for this liberalization, which actually nullifies the project-grant policy,
our basic research investigators could hardly function at all.

What are the specific ways in which project support hampers the
basic scientist and therefore handicaps progress in basic research?
The most important ways are these:—

1. *It wastes the time of applicant investigators writing up detailed project descriptions for explorations into the unknown.*

As already indicated, there is no value in having basic investigators write up plans for "exploring the unknown," writing annual progress reports about such plans, and so on. Anyone who has ever
climbed a mountain or explored a cave knows how your plans change
almost from minute to minute. How can one describe such a trip
in advance? The most you can do at the start of such a study is to
have a broad goal and a plan for your first step into the unknown.
Detail beyond this is more likely to be wrong than right, and so is a
sheer waste of time.

The project policy is a way of looking over the shoulders of basic
investigators and implies a lack of confidence in them. If we have

decided that basic research pays off, why can't we select our good scientists, support them as the Renaissance patrons did, and have enough faith in them and in our ability to select them to feel sure our patronage will pay off *in the long run?*

2. *It wastes the time of the committee scientists who "advise" the various granting agencies concerning which project to support.*

For example, a prominent scientist living in California who's a member of say four grant-allocating committees which usually meet in the east, must make four trips a year to attend these four committee meetings. He probably spends at least twice as much time traveling as he does actually working in the committee. Is this an efficient use of his time? At present a considerable amount of the valuable time of many of our best senior scientists is spent shuttling across the country from one committee meeting to another making "decisions" which, given the circumstances outlined above, are meaningless. The more basic research money available, the more time our senior scientists have to spend, distributing it. Therefore more money, if dispensed in the same way, may tend to slow down basic research. Dr. Richter has said: "Large funds encourage great enterprises—great experimental designs. They encourage great 'teams of workers.' They take good research men away from their work to direct many technicians. The use of such large sums from the public treasury for research must be justified—public-spirited men are likely to want to know how the funds have been used. This means that we, members of this and similar committees, as men who are responsible for the distribution of funds from the public treasury, are naturally prompted to play safe, not to gamble with public funds. Sensitive to these responsibilities we feel ourselves urged to ask for details of designs, expenditures—we hesitate to give the researcher a free hand. We have to ask ourselves whether this is a wise, farsighted policy."

3. It *fragments the financial support of an investigator's laboratory into a maze of separate accounts, each of which has a slightly different set of restrictions placed on it.*

This places the laboratory director (the senior scientist) in about the same position as the housewife who each week divides her husband's pay among a series of fruit jars, and then spends several hours a week deciding from which jar she will take money for different purchases. There are some who defend this "system" on the grounds that it is never safe to put all one's eggs in one basket. They believe that the researcher is better off if he can apply to many sources for support.

Where is the evidence to support this belief? The attitude implies that many committee decisions are wrong. It assumes, as is possibly true for the reasons already stated, that our best scientists often cannot wisely select between basic projects. Therefore, the argument runs, we must not put "all our eggs in one basket." This might be called applying the "uncertainty principle" to the dispersing of research funds. This concept has its place in science, but not when applied in this way.

The "fruit jar" project system provides only a precarious hand-to-mouth existence. Since today almost all new basic research laboratories must be built up on this "boot-strap" basis, it is not surprising that new ones are slow in developing. Trying to establish and run a laboratory without any "capital reserves" and in competition with well established laboratories is just as precarious as starting and running a business under similar conditions. Though no one knows the figures, it is certain that our "laboratory bankruptcy rate" is high indeed. This is a wasteful way to establish laboratories and to run research and employ scientists. Most of our famous basic scientists have to apply for grants to different agencies several times a year in order to refill their "fruit jars" and keep their laboratories going. Why should highly qualified researchers have to justify their continued function several times a year to groups of men who, generally, know less about the proposals than the applicants?

4. *It provides no economic security for the technicians and scientists hired to work on such grants. They are working only for an individual scientist and have no more than a one year guarantee of a job. They earn no pension rights except Social Security.*

From the standpoint of young scientists or technicians dependent for their living on the renewal of annual grants, the project way of life is as economically hazardous as Russian roulette. No one can prove that many high school or college students are avoiding science as a career because of these precarious working relationships. Nor do we know how many young wives have steered their husbands away from such precarious careers. But a good many indirect clues plus some common sense analysis make it seem quite certain that this is the case.

If basic science is to compete on an equal basis with business administration and with the applied science professions, it must be able to offer young people lifetime careers with financial and other rewards whch are reasonably competitive. With all the talk about the demand for young scientists, it will no doubt surprise some readers that many young scientists are working under such uncertain financial arrangements. The current demand for young physicists and mathematicians has helped to improve the financial returns in these fields. But the young biological scientists still have difficulty finding good, secure jobs. It is this group I am thinking of at the moment. To be sure, they can find research jobs of the temporary type I have described or poorly paid teaching jobs. But, because of the economic insecurity in basic research, the dominating movement of science personnel in biology, as in the physical sciences, is toward applied research in government and business where there is economic security.

If, as suggested in a previous chapter, practicing scientists take over the function of teaching in our high schools, and if we establish the principle of paying scientists for writing scientific papers and also raise their salaries, we would begin to restore basic science to a reasonable economic status.

5. *The liberalization which permits investigators to switch the aims of their projects makes an absurdity of the policy of supporting projects. It is an indirect way of supporting people in the guise of supporting projects.*

What is the sense of bringing many of our best senior scientists to Washington or New York to decide between the relative merits of applications, when the project investigators are then to be free to switch their goals without referring back to the grant committee? The talents and wisdom of our senior scientists would be put to better use if we undertook the support of individuals and institutions. Then these men would need only to select those younger men each year who would be chosen as "established investigators" assured of whatever sums, within reason, they needed to pursue their goals.

These committee members could also decide on the financing and organizing of new research centers to meet the new and expanding needs of scientific development. They could avoid wasting their energies on a large number of "project" decisions which can now be ignored by the project investigator.

The committees could then devote their energies to finding scientists with creative imagination, and supporting them no matter where their imagination or research leads them. Experience demonstrates that creative scientists can be identified. Creative imagination is a quality which once acquired is likely to endure and evidence of its operation is not too difficult to recognize. Good scientists know the quality when they see it. Committees composed of our good scien-

tists would be able to select, for established investigators, those who
have repeatedly demonstrated creative imagination in their work.

The support of individual scientists and/or institutions rather than
specified projects has long been the practice in Europe. The "established investigatorships" of the American Heart Association started
a few years ago and more recently those established by the National
Institutes of Health and the National Science Foundation are based
on this approach to the problem of giving support to individual
scientists of proven capacity. Unfortunately, all of these are for
limited periods and most of them do not provide for support of the
investigator's laboratory. He must still propose projects for that
support. These positions should also carry an annual unrestricted
grant of reasonable size to provide at least a working "reserve." Both
the number of these positions and their length of tenure should be
greatly increased until this becomes the dominant way of supporting
basic research.

6. *In a competitive field such as basic research it asks quite a
bit of human nature, to require basic scientists to put their best ideas
on paper and mail them off for consideration by a group of men they
don't even know as the project system does.*

It is well known that there is a certain amount of hestitation about
putting one's best ideas into grant requests. After all, *having a new
idea and proving it* is the business of a basic scientist. And there
isn't much "pay-offs" for being the second or third or fourth one to
make a discovery. In fact it's hard to get the third and fourth reports published unless there is additional data or unless the basic
subject is of great importance. Dr. Richter frankly tackled this
delicate point when he said: "Let us be careful how we handle a
researcher's ideas. They belong to him. When he puts them on application forms, let us not broadcast them, scatter them far and wide
to scrupulous and unscrupulous hands. Public agencies do this now
with the result that authorship of ideas is often forgotten or ignored.
The researcher's satisfaction comes from finishing a job—his own.
He is human. It may have taken him years to work out his ideas.
In wartime, yes, all ideas must be pooled and as quickly as possible.
But not in peacetime."

Why should we try to finance basic research with such a psychologically unsound system as the project system? Perhaps the already
mentioned changes in N. I. H. grants, which permit the principal investigator to veer entirely away from his stated project, if he so
chooses, were due, in part at least, to a recognition of these factors.

As already indicated, this liberalization of project support policy makes nonsense out of the basic "policy" being discussed. For, if the projects approved are only proxies for those actually carried out, why should first-rate scientists spend long hours passing on the relative merits of the proxy proposals of other scientists who spent long hours writing up the proxies?

In summary, we may say that except for the relatively few "established investigators," the main policy of the several different private and public agencies distributing medical research funds, most of which are intended to support basic work, is to distribute their money largely on a project basis. Each operating agency maintains an elaborate administrative staff to distribute these funds and each overlaps the other's categories in many different ways.

We have seen that the system is not even trusted by N. I. H. to give wise scientific decisions, for the investigator is now free to reverse his goals completely without the approval of N. I. H. The system usually results in unnecessary paperwork and administrative meetings.

The system of multiple granting agencies, has created a tremendous hierarchy of scientific administrators. These jobs rather than research are the jobs in science with maximum economic advantages. Because of this, it is likely that many *good basic scientists* are forced, for economic reasons, to spend their time as *poor administrators*. The public's money is being wasted. Even more important, the time of many of our best basic scientists is also being wasted by this cumbersome overlapping system for distributing research funds. The personal economic insecurity resulting from this method of operation is driving first-rate scientists out of basic research. The net affect of all these factors plays a major role in the current shortage of both science teachers and students. Young people observe how their elders work and live and the insecurity and dissatisfaction with the working conditions in science (especially in the biological sciences) has not been overlooked by our youngsters in high school and college. This situation must surely play a significant role in directing educational choices away from biology and from science generally. We hear a lot about "dedicated" scientists who work for love of science rather than for money. Dedication is something that *develops* in a field. It cannot be looked upon as a recruitment aid. And some of the "dedication" may not be quite as deep as it appears. A man in middle age with a family can't easily change his work. He must stay "dedicated," if he wants to keep up his mortgage payments.

Over the long run you can't power a modern science program with "dedication."

Two main steps should be taken for choosing and tending our scientific "horses." Step number one is for some *non-governmental* agency, possibly the Scientific Manpower Commission, to establish a national scientific personnel system. This system would collect education and experience records, reprints of publications, and other evidences of scientific work on *all registered* scientists. The system should be *established and operated by scientists and be democratically controlled by them.* Safeguards can be set up to prevent any abuse that might occur. The file should receive the same "confidential" treatment and legal protection now given to hospital medical records.

Is it not worse than foolish for a scientific technical society such as ours to fail to study the performance of our scientists? We spend billions to educate and train young scientists, and then make no effort to insure that they have the tools and environment to function optimally. We do not even make an effort to follow their careers and find out how productive they are as individuals, so we can modify our educational system to correct any deficiencies disclosed. Contrast our attitudes toward scientists with the elaborate statistics kept on baseball and football players and pure-bred livestock!

This science personnel record system would make it possible to develop some operational analyses necessary for administrative planning which seem to be lacking now. It would also make it possible to study our individual scientific "horses" with somewhat the same precision that the professional gambler uses when he studies the race horses. Such a system would tend to place more emphasis on scientific merit and less on "personality."

We would in this way have readily available professional histories which could guide us in choosing those individuals worthy of "lifetime investigator" support. Such a system would also help insure that the output of scientists was properly evaluated and their professional progress related to their output. Science would have the basic personnel system needed to provide overall operational statistics on scientific personnel—the kind of data so badly needed and so generally unavailable at present.

The second step would be to enlarge, if necessary, the present National Research Council's committee system to serve all national agencies, private as well as governmental, which have funds to distribute for basic research. We should put all our basic research funds in this "one basket" and then see that the "basket" is properly tended. The National Research Council already serves some of the small private agencies in precisely this way. The existing procedures can simply be expanded and improved to meet this larger need. If the "basket" is under the independent control of a distinguished Board of Directors containing a majority of scientists together with representatives of government, business, labor, the professions and the lay public, it should not become the special preserve of a small clique. Adequate safeguards can be set up to prevent this happening.

The selection of individuals and institutions for long term support will require more careful study than choosing between small research projects. No doubt, occasional errors will occur in such a system also. In an imperfect world there probably is no perfect, foolproof system for making any kind of decision. But society does choose between people every day when it chooses someone to head a tremendous business, a great university, an established institute, or a science department. Is it so much more difficult to establish criteria whereby individuals could qualify for lifetime support? The generous support of established investigators and their work (either directly or through support of institutions) on a lifetime basis would automatically finance the research of younger men working with them. This would cut down the total number of "decisions" which the National Research Council committees would need to make and so save valuable time of senior scientists. Administrative costs would be materially reduced and efficiency distinctly enhanced.

Thus far I have spoken as though basic research money should be distributed solely to support "Established Investigators" or institutions. There is one other role which the National Research Council should perform which might lead to an exception to this general principle. The National Research Council should systematically and continuously study the advancing frontier of basic science. When neglected research sectors were noted, steps should be taken to encourage someone to enter them. This encouragement might necessitate the committee's sponsoring specific projects in such a new sector in order to open it up. As soon as others took up the work, the National Research Council committees would no doubt withdraw. These National Research Council committees should have nothing to do with developmental or applied research. The committees should also study scientific education at all levels and serve in an advisory capacity in the field of science to the National Education Commission which was proposed in an earlier chapter.

Individual private agencies would continue their valuable fund raising and educational activities. The National Research Council committees would distribute the funds collected in accordance with the general objectives set down by the private and public agencies being served.

With such an administrative set-up, American science would have a policy and decision-making system adequate to its modern responsibilities. It would have an organization capable of identifying and adequately supporting those scientists who demonstrate their scientific ability. It would also have a system for continuously studying the advancing frontier of science; a mechanism whereby research gaps could be closed rather than waiting for a chance to close them; and a body competent to advise on the national aspects of scientific education.

Chapter X

OUR SCIENTIFIC NERVOUS SYSTEM

Science is fundamentally ideas—ideas about nature. Only secondarily do these ideas get translated into useful tools for improved health or improved "hardware." So, ideas are the real raw materials on which our modern, specialized, technical society depends for its survival. Progress comes only through the discovery of new information or through the development of new ideas about old information.

A new idea derives from the association of two or more old ideas *in someone's head*. Frequently, the same new idea occurs to several people at about the same time. This is not too difficult to understand, for specialists interested in a particular sector of science are more or less reading and thinking about the same unsolved problems existing in their sector. When two or more relevant ideas (ideas which "fit together") exist and are more or less lying free waiting to be associated, it is not surprising that two or more scientists notice their relevance at approximately the same time.

This situation is rather like a jig-saw puzzle which is being solved by several players at once. Often, two or more of them will reach for the same piece at the same instant. The more people playing, the more often this will occur. Also, the more nearly the puzzle reaches solution, the easier it becomes to fit in the final pieces. If we want more new science ideas, the way to get them is to get more people playing scientific "jig-saw" and facilitate the speed with which the discovery of new "pieces"—ideas—are made known to the players.

The better informed a scientist is and the more he is aware of ideas relevant to the scientific sector in which he is working, the better is his chance of making a new idea association, of discovering where a new "piece" fits.

It has been authoritatively reported that the average time between date of receipt and date of publication of articles in scientific journals is much shorter in Soviet Russia than in the U. S. Moreover, the Russians translate and distribute American articles in much less time than we accomplish the reverse operation. The reports we have had on their literature handling indicate that the average Soviet scientist has perhaps a 12 to 24-month literature advantage over the average American scientist. It is also said that in some fields we are able to learn about our own research more easily and quickly by translating the better organized Soviet journals reporting on our work than by searching through the great number of journals in which it was originally scattered here.

Since new ideas are the basis of improving our standard of living, we have a real stake in facilitating the discovery, transmission and communication of ideas between scientists.

In considering the origin, transmission, storage and use of scientific ideas, it is helpful to compare the system with a human "nervous system." The scientists working in their laboratories are the "sense organs" of society. They are feeling, seeing, hearing nature with their own sense organs or with special scientific "sensory" instru- tinuous state of change, our social "sense organs" must be ever alert ments. Since the world—especially the world of today—is in a con- so we are kept "in touch" with the world—the nature—in which we live.

In order to be transmitted as "sensory messages" the findings and discoveries made in the laboratories must usually be written and published as a "To whom it may concern" report in a scientific journal. This stage is comparable to the transmission of a sensory nerve impulse over a nerve fiber(s) to reach the "social brain"—the library.

In the "social brain" the report ("message") is analyzed, classified and stored ("memorized") and so retained for future retrieval ("recall") and use. The "social memory" device provides the means whereby scientific ideas may be retained, sometimes for centuries, waiting to be united and coordinated with other ideas in order to provide a basis for new technical (applied science) advances or for new basic science discoveries.

Since such changes modify the nature of our society and keep it constantly evolving, the circle is thus completed. The need for continuous never ending study by *all* kinds of scientific sense organs is apparent. With the increasing number of laboratories ("sense organs") and reports ("messages"), it is obvious that our scientific "nervous system" can work well only if ideas pass *quickly* from the publication step through the steps which precede filing and then remain accessible to any one who may later wish to use them. The system is now breaking down in this country because of many defects at every step along this pathway.

We have been aware of some of these defects for a number of years but have not done much about them. The recent Soviet scientific successes have made some of us take a new look at the Soviet as well as our own handling of the literature problem. One important scientist who has done this is **Dr. E. Finley Carter, Director of the Stanford Research Institute.** In a talk summarized in the *New York Times,* he said that there has been for years a "... continuous crash program in the Soviet Union to translate foreign technical periodicals and distribute the data to those concerned. We in the United States have no such effective facility for collecting and disseminating scientific information."

He noted that the Russians had been accused of withholding data necessary to track their satellites [Sputniks I and II]. He stated that, "four days after the first satellite was launched, [his] institute received a translation of a Soviet article describing in detail what the satellite would do, how it would be observed, the nature of the signals which would be transmitted, and so forth." The article had been published in June [1957] in the Soviet amateur radio journal. He commented, "If a four-month delay in translation of an article of such importance was typical, it indicates that we are either tragically slow, or that we have not accorded enough significance to what others have been doing—or both."

He urged us to quickly establish "a facility to store and retrieve technical literature from all countries. . . . We must break down barriers to cross-communication and idea-stimulation inherent in our cumbersome and complex security system."

He pointed out that for years it had been known in the United States that the Russians had an elaborate system to obtain the proceedings of technical meetings in the West as well as specialized periodicals. This material is rushed to the All-Union Institute of Scientific and Technical Information which analyzes, abstracts, cross-indexes and then distributes the information. He quoted a member of the National Science Foundation in Washington as saying that the best way to improve American coverage in a given field was to obtain the abstracts issued by this Soviet agency and translate the material back into English. Of the work of the Soviet agency he said: "This is no leisurely operation, carried out in bureaucratic surroundings. It is a continuous crash program."

Few will dispute that Dr. Carter has reported the main facts and correctly appraised the situation. It is apparent that *because of our inadequate science communication system, our scientists are working under a severe handicap compared with Soviet scientists.*

What can be done to correct this situation?

Let us begin by considering the problem from the standpoint of the author of the report. Many scientists might not admit it, but the inner personal reason they publish reports about their experiments is that they enjoy telling others about their experience. Though the rigid style of most science papers may obscure the underlying enjoyment, it is there none-the-less. Scientists find pleasure in making discoveries about nature, in finding a flaw in a previously accepted theory. Of course, they often follow their criticism of the old theory by offering a new one they believe better fits the facts.

They are essentially detectives—detectives trying to unravel the puzzles of nature. Like Sherlock Holmes, they like to describe their searches, especially the successful ones that lead to new information. So, their enjoyment is complete only when they report their work and expose it to the critical scrutiny of their fellow scientists. The report thus makes it possible for other scientists to repeat these experiments as a part of their appraisal and to confirm or refute the claim to new discovery. The test of independent repetition, so important to science in avoiding prolonged acceptance of error, is absolutely dependent on widespread dissemination of research findings that reach interested fellow scientists, now and in future.

A second value of scientific reporting is that one's fellow-scientists evaluate one's worth on the basis of published work. Professional advancement often depends on the quantity and quality of one's publications. Unfortunately, as we have seen in the previous chapter, this appraisal can be extremely haphazard.

Considerations such as these make clear why scientists oppose indiscriminate use of the "secret" label on research. When the give and take of the published report is stopped, research loses much of its stimulation and enjoyment.

Next let's look at the journals from the business standpoint. As pointed out in a previous chapter, our early science organizations were really social clubs—whose members had a common interest in some aspect of science. The business arrangements of our basic science journals still reflect that background. Because of the relatively few readers of basic science journals, publication costs are high. Because the readers neither buy very much nor directly sell any "hardware" the journals' advertising rates are low and their budgets small. Some of them survive only because a foundation or philanthropic agency underwrites their losses. The budgets are, in fact, so small that there is no money to pay the scientific authors of the articles. There is not even money to pay the volunteer "referee" editors who do the major screening job for the editors.

I have already suggested that scientists are willing to write for nothing because publication really is the final step in the experiment and their enjoyment and professional advancement depend on it. But it is worth considering what might be the effect of paying authors for this writing. The one scientific journal which does pay its authors, Scientific American, certainly has the highest readability index of all. Surely the editor who can pay his authors must feel a little freer to demand higher literary standards. Perhaps the proverbial dullness of scientific writing is related to this business situation.

The writer for a woman's magazine gives some suggestions for making hors d'oeuvres and is paid two or three hundred dollars. The writer of a scientific article telling how to make a vaccine which will protect millions from a dread disease gets nothing. Isn't this a strange form of "free" enterprise?

What about the matter of the free editing? Why should thousands of *anonymous* "referee" editors drop their own research work or *give* up some of their evenings to "referee" or screen hundreds of thousands of manuscripts for nothing? This must come close to the ultimate in "dedication." Of course one "pay-off" is the sense of "belonging" to the "elite" who are requested, presumably because of mastery of their field, to do this "labor of love." The other "pay-off" is that screening manuscripts containing research reports on work in your immediate field of interest does help you keep abreast of the directions in which others (your scientific competitors) are thinking and working. In view of the literature communication difficulties we are considering here, this is not an inconsequential "pay-off." Nevertheless, there's no reason why this referee editing should be done free.

If these anonymous screening editors were paid, it would be possible to make two demands on them which cannot now be made. First, they could be required to review manuscripts more promptly. Delays are often considerable at present. Second, they would not be permitted to operate behind the current curtain of anonymity, a curtain apparently erected to protect them from having to devote considerable time to explaining their decisions. Though understandable under the present circumstances, this arrangement has many shortcomings. A scientist who has written a report and had it criticized, especially if it has been rejected, knows how necessary it is to discuss the criticisms directly with the critic in order to get a real understanding of the shortcomings. It is most disheartening and frustrating to be unable to do this. But an even more frustrating experience is to try to carry on such discussion with an anonymous referee editor with the fulltime editor serving as an intermediary. Scientific reports, often the result of months or years of painstaking and thoughtful research, deserve something better than the cavalier treatment of anonymous dismissal.

Another weakness in our scientific "nervous system" is the scientific meeting. One aspect of the problem is presented in a letter which appeared in *Science* of May 10, 1957. It read: "There is a statement in "Social aspects of Science" *Science* 125, 145 (25 Jan. 1957) to the effect that our recent Conference on the Practical Utilization of Recorded Knowledge found it necessary to hold parts of its deliberation behind closed doors and to refrain from publicizing the full record of these 'confidential' sessions.

"The sessions were not *confidential*, but rather attendance was *limited* to those in various subject areas who might contribute best to these sessions . . . As per plan, *summaries* of these sessions have been published in the book . . . which records the proceedings of the conference. [Italics added.]

"We believe that the technique of limiting attendance in certain types of meetings helps to stimulate discussion by special interest groups who might otherwise be inhibited from presenting their views in public. This was indeed the case in these sessions."

One group of physicists whose field has become crowded holds private, unannounced meetings. Otherwise, they say, their meetings would be so crowded they would get nothing done. Perhaps so, but the possibility of reorganizing their meetings, using modern group discussion and large conference methods, have been ignored.

These two examples illustrate only limited aspects of this weakness in our scientific "nervous system." Our national and regional conferences attended by hundreds and sometimes thousands of scientists are still run essentially as they were fifty years ago when they were held for a small fraction of the number who now attend. To accomodate the increased numbers of reports, they are now compressed to 10 or 15 minutes and discussion is usually limited to 5 minutes. The large number of papers necessitates sub-division of these conferences into a large number of sessions. The assignment of papers is on some rather arbitrary basis. Consequently a scientist must rush from one session to another to hear the different papers that interest him. The information in these brief papers is often so compressed as to make them unintelligible to all except real "insiders" in that field, and, of course, the short discussion time makes a farce of the word "discussion."

Small informal talks and conferences and more formal symposia are constantly being held in various scientific institutions in this country. Most of these have relatively small audiences. Many of them are of the "off the top of the head" variety which deal with speculations at the frontiers of science—considering the far goals and the likely next steps to be tried at the frontier, and so on. Despite their informality many of the speakers are scientific leaders, foreign and domestic, who cannot possibly get around to the many small groups who would profit from hearing their talk.

"Off the record" speculation at such meetings is precisely the kind of most value in stimulating young scientists and potential scientists. This also is the information of the very greatest value to the active research worker. The active investigator listening to leading scientists talk about the frontier of the field he is interested in, gains confidence that he knows where the frontier is and understands it. In a fast moving situation, this is always of great value. The investigator may learn facts which will either encourage him to follow a "pet" idea, or to discard it if he learns that the idea has already been tried. He may decide the approach he has been considering is not so good as another suggested by the talk.

We must find a way to bring these small conferences to *all* who could profit from attending them, and bring them in a form which makes them real instruments of communication. Our large science meetings have become a ritual and have lost most of their original value as instruments of communication—so much so that many scientists admit that they go to them not for scientific but for personal and administrative reasons.

There are modern techniques that could solve most of the conference problems. Most of our conferences are organized by "free" volunteers who have had no training in conference planning techniques. It takes a great deal of skill and organization to conduct a large meeting in such a manner that *all* participate and profit. But it can be done, and science can get the money to pay experts to do the job instead of relying on overworked amateurs.

Closed circuit TV is an ideal tool to bring much of this kind of informal audio-visual information to interested scientists. Thus far, this tool has been used in science only to a limited degree—mostly by the drug industry. We should consider establishing a national system which would schedule, produce and distribute this kind of information over a nationwide hook-up. We might be able to establish such a system as an adjunct of existing commercial TV and thus avoid the necessity of duplicating studio facilities. In view of the existing time lag in literature publication and distribution, it is clear that such an arrangement would be of major importance in speeding the distribution of scientific knowledge. America certainly has the technical "know-how" to work that one out, in a hurry. Doing this and adopting modern conference techniques can do much to relieve our immediate communication problem while we work out the more difficult problem of library reorganization.

When it comes to running a literature system we can learn a great deal by studying the Soviet system. Let us look at their set-up and make some comparisons. In the Soviet Union, writing and editing articles and translating foreign articles is an important source of the scientists' income. The Soviets use money as though they were capitalists—as an incentive to encourage their scientists to write and communicate with each other. Ironically, as we have seen, we run our journals on a communistic "free" basis!

In this country until recently, the problem of translating articles in foreign journals was left to the individual scientist to solve as best he could. Most of them have had to ignore much of the foreign literature, especially Soviet literature, for there are few Americans who can read Russian. Some steps have been taken to translate and distribute some of the Soviet literature, but little or nothing has been done about translating other foreign literature. Eastern Europe, Japan and China are all producing scientific work that is becoming increasingly important.

As Dr. Carter indicated in the talk quoted earlier, the Soviets have an All-Union Institute of Scientific and Technical Information. This Institute serves as the coordination center for controlling the entire Soviet science communication system. Part of this system is a central scientific translation bureau which employs 2,500 full-time and 10,000 to 20,000 part-time, highly-qualified translators, to make sure their scientists keep abreast of *all progress in science*. This bureau receives essentially *all* the scientific journals of the *entire world*. It is said to translate over 11,000 foreign scientific journals. We do fewer than 200. It translates, abstracts, screens, indexes, stores and distributes these reports, essentially as it does its own scientists' reports.

Another aspect of their system worth special mention is their extensive system of "express" newsletters, similar to weekly business newsletters published in this country. They contain brief items from both the Soviet and foreign scientific literature—items thought to be of special value or significance to the scientists in the particular field the "express" paper serves. In science we have essentially nothing that compares with this system. The weekly *Science News Letter* which covers all of science in 10 or 12 pages and two or three industry sponsored papers are the only comparable publications we have. These are useful, but they are limited as compared with what the Soviets have.

To appreciate the importance of these "express" journals, imagine yourself a Soviet scientist interested in a field in which such a journal exists. Your "express" journal brings you brief accounts of the most important recent work published *in the entire world*. In short, you have *several thousand people constantly at work doing library research for you,* screening and sorting both your own country's reports and reports from all over the world of interest in your field. If you want to read the whole article it is already available *in the Russian* language. Such a setup must contribute enormously to the intellectual efficiency of Soviet science.

Now let's consider the library—the "social brain"—and what is involved in storing ("memorizing") and retrieving ("recalling") scientific ideas. Just as in storing anything, there are both efficient and inefficient ways of storing ideas. Efficiency in a library can only be judged in terms of how costly it is to store the ideas and how easily they can be retrieved. To present this problem adequately it is necessary to consider briefly the history of modern science and its libraries.

The essential point in understanding our present predicament, is that modern science began as a relatively static descriptive and classificatory matter. The early scientists were called "natural historians." They carefully described, recorded and classified objects— minerals, plants, animals and so on. Gradually, this task reached a stage where certain natural classification schemes became evident. The known animals and plants were grouped into families, genuses, species, and so on. Linnaeus' classification was static, but Darwin's studies led him beyond this static classification concept so he came to recognize the underlying dynamics of biology. Out of this recognition grew his book "Origin of Species"—which presented his theory of evolution. Similar transformations from static to dynamic science have occurred in every area. Medical research has passed from the static stage of anatomy to the dynamic stage of physiology and pathology. Static mineralogy has become dynamic modern chemistry and paleontology.

Libraries built to store static information present no serious classification problem. Static descriptions may be stored even on so arbitrary a basis as the alphabet. The dictionary is a good illustration of such a classification plan.

But when a science becomes dynamic, the problem becomes more complex. Then the interest centers on interactions taking place in time between two or more different objects or forces. The question is: Under which item of the several interacting ones should the dynamic *experiment,* not the static *description* of yore, be classified?

Another aspect of this problem is the rate at which science libraries grow. Studies of past library growth have shown an increase of about 5% a year. At this rate shelf-space would need to double every few years. It is not difficult to realize that, if you don't have a good classification system, retrieval in a library to which millions of items are constantly being added becomes very difficult. The fact is that we are already in a state of crisis. We need to establish a dynamic classification scheme which will provide as sound and easily operated a storage system as the alphabet (or Dewey decimal system) provided for static data.

Surprisingly enough, there is actually a library in existence which has solved this problem in a limited, but complicated field of science—endocrinology. The existing working model is the library of Dr. Hans Selye's Institute of Medicine and Experimental Surgery in Montreal, Canada. I have studied this model and am convinced that its basic classification idea could be adapted and expanded to meet the literature classification problem in most areas of science. Dr. Selye's library has been organized on the basis of a unique classification scheme which he devised. He had the rare opportunity of establishing and running a library built to serve his needs, whereas most other scientists have had to adapt themselves to the practices of the libraries in the institutions in which they work. But he started his career quite early in the development period of the dynamic field of endocrinology, and so was able to develop his own dynamic classification and filing system. The details of this system are somewhat technical, and not pertinent to this discussion—the important point is that a model is in existence *which works* and which shows approximately how a larger system built on the same basic idea would work. The system is described fully in Dr. Selye's book called "Stress." So far as I have been able to discover, there is not another institutional library in the world organized on these dynamic principles.

Of course, it will be costly to reorganize our scientific libraries along the lines of these dynamic classification principles. However, anyone who studies this problem cannot escape the conclusion that we *must change* our present system. In such circumstances, the cost problem is irrelevant. It is a matter of the life of our library system. The system is sick. It suffers from a kind of arteriosclerosis, which is slowing down our scientific "reaction time." Our libraries are also becoming too "forgetful" to be adequate to our needs. (*Today it is often cheaper to repeat research than to search for the report on earlier work.*) When this is true of such vital institutions as our science libraries, we have no alternative except to spend *whatever it takes to cure the ill*. The longer we wait the more difficult and costly the cure will be, for the problem is growing bigger all the time. I am convinced that a National Science Library system similar to Selye's system, together with a national translating and abstracting system and a good system of "Express News Letters" would increase the overall efficiency of our scientists by a factor of at least two. Our inadequate publication, translation, classification, storage and retrieval system; the resulting slow, totally inadequate system of distributing our scientific information, and our antiquated conference methods, constitute a key scientific weakness and account in large degree for cumulating defeats in the scientific realm.

If we are going to attack the scientific communication problem in the fundamental ways outlined in this chapter, we must accept the idea that libraries are our "social brains," our memory systems for storing the information obtained in the "sense organs"—the research laboratories. Just as the brain and nervous system is the most important organ of the body, so reports and the journals which carry them to other scientists and to libraries where they are stored for others to use later are our most important social organ. Our civilization depends on the continued vitality of our "social brains." By storing previous knowledge which the schools use in educating the oncoming generations, the libraries also make it possible for society to replace the parts of its "nervous sytem" and so continue the life of the social organism in a fresh and dynamic state. To say, as has frequently been said, that we can't afford to spend a few millions to support our journals, or to modernize our libraries, or to support

some properly organized conferences or a TV network or other communication channels needed, is like hearing a man say he can't afford
the medicine or surgery necessary to save his life. A society which
says it "can't afford" to maintain its own "nervous system" is showing signs of senility.

PART II

THE LONG-RANGE VIEW

In addition to the science and related education crisis
considered in the previous chapters, this country must deal
with four other major problems. These are of a more political-economic nature than the ones considered previously.
Since there are ways in which science and education can
help in their solution, I hope my discussion of the scientific aspects of these political-economic matters will prove
useful. They may be stated briefly as follows:

First, we face the danger that our automated industry
will produce more things than we can consume and result
in chronic mass unemployment. A second danger is that
inadequate use of excess leisure will lead to a soft-headed
welfare-state economy lacking incentives to stimulate individual initiative. Third is the possibility that cheap atomic
energy may disrupt our economy by outmoding present
economic values. These first three problems are at present
more or less confined to Western Europe and the United
States though other nations including those in the Soviet-
bloc are moving toward a similar situation. The fourth
threat to us is that uncontrolled population growth now
occurring in the underdeveloped countries can create population pressures (surplus people) which may, if unchecked, disrupt civilization on a world scale within the next
few centuries.

Looming even larger than these dangers is the awesome
one of annihilation by nuclear war or of less dramatic but
no less real internal exhaustion through prolonged cold war.

It is my belief that satisfactory solution of these problems depends on our adopting as a major policy the objective of helping the underdeveloped countries move toward
standards of living comparable to ours by the year 2000
(to name a reasonable date).

In the following chapter I will present the reasons why
we should adopt such a policy, as well as suggestions concerning principles to be followed in carrying them out.

CHAPTER XI

SCIENCE AND SOCIAL MUTATION

In recent years, science has often been accused of causing the great problems that have come with excess things, leisure and people. These accusations are usually coupled with a challenge that science *do something* to solve the problem it has created. As a scientist, I accept the accusation for basically it is a great compliment to science. The problems complained of need be only relatively temporary maladjustments. They are by-products of the marvelously beneficial works that science has produced, and are due to the fact that society has not yet learned to adjust its organization and operations as rapidly as science-induced changes demand. I not only accept the charge that science is responsible, but I also accept the demand that science *do something* to solve these problems. In the remainder of this book I will try to "do something" helpful by analyzing the problems and by suggesting some changes in our policies and operations, which would help bring our social machinery into harmony with our scientific machinery. In doing this I will try to apply knowledge which I gained from my years of work in the field of public health.

Many of our public health programs have elements in common with the problem of foreign aid in that they are generally designed to improve health in some "underdeveloped" area of our own country. The need of underdeveloped nations is for improved "public health" in which the term is broadened to include educational and economic development. Experience has shown that public health measures get carried out only when some individual or agency—usually some county, state or federal political body—is willing to support it. Therefore, the public health official who wants to "sell" a program must usually be prepared to answer questions such as these: What are the reasons for conducting the program? Who will benefit from it? How much will it cost? Who should pay for it? Why should they support this program as compared with other possible competing proposals? It seems to me that the many who have spoken in favor of foreign aid have not yet adequately answered all these questions for the American taxpayer. And the taxpayer is entitled to complete answers to all of them. It is up to the advocates of such a policy to present logical reasons to indicate that such a program will be useful to America and worth the cost to Americans. I hope to do this.

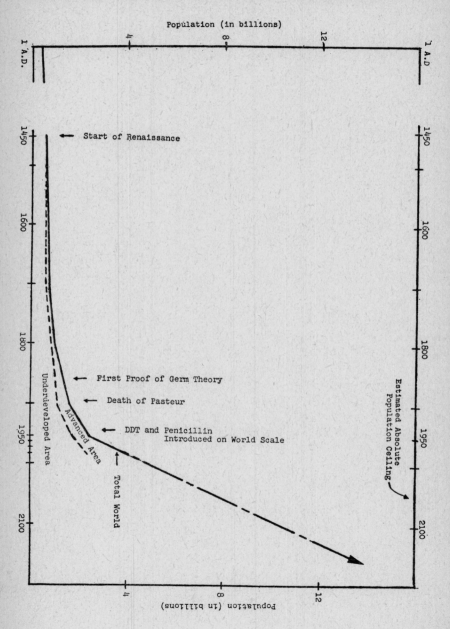

The problems we Americans face have never been more confused than now. Let us see if we can find out how we and the rest of the world got into our present state. A good starting point for considering this is to study the population curves in the chart on page 94.

This chart shows only the development of population in the present millennium. There is no need to deal with the prior one thousand millenia of human history. Only a few critical changes (social mutations) occurred during all the previous years of man's social evolution. For present purposes we can simply list them as follows: 1. Evolution of Stone-Age man from his pre-man ancestry. 2. Development of Tribal man. 3. Development of Agricultural (civilized) village man. 4. Development of Political (city-state) man.

Though the changes in man's early development led slowly to both qualitative and quantitative changes in population, they were so relatively slow as compared to those of the past 500 years that it is difficult to fix their beginning and ending.

The fifth significant change in man's social development is presented by the chart. It shows the effect of man's latest social mutation—the development of scientific or "advanced" man—on world population growth. Advanced man split off from the main—underdeveloped—body of the human race, migrated into Europe and America and there produced a revolutionary new society based on modern science, agriculture, industry and medicine. His new tool for accomplishing this was the scientific method of thinking.

Prior to the birth of modern science, which really means the birth of the Italian Renaissance around 1450, the population of the civilized world was largely concentrated in the countries surrounding the Mediterranean, in the areas we now call the Middle and Far East, in India and China and contiguous countries. Europe was relatively sparsely settled. America had not been discovered and most of the rest of the world was peopled with more or less uncivilized tribes.

Until the Renaissance, the world's total population had, because of frequent setbacks from famine and disease, grown slowly for many centuries. Its technology was progressing slowly. It had to be slow because technical growth can only take place if available food increases to enable more people to be freed from the soil to engage in scientific and technical work.

Why did the Renaissance sweep North and West into Europe and from there to North America and why did it not also move South and East into the more settled world areas? One reason probably was that in contrast to the rest of the world, Europe was relatively sparse-

ly settled and so afforded a relative degree of social and political independence. The status of Europe in terms of population and resources, as compared with older parts of the world was equivalent
to that of America in the eighteenth and nineteenth centuries. The
natural wealth available in relation to the number of people was relatively high. Therefore, northern and western Europe was the frontier
of the then known civilized world, the place where freedom and opportunity were greatest. The older countries, the ones we now call
underdeveloped, were already in a state of semi-disintegration and
were falling back from their previous "advanced" heights. Their
agricultural, health, industrial and political organization had proved
inadequate to break the cycle of relative over-population, mal-
nourishment, insufficient capital, bureaucracy, and so on. A second
reason that the Renaissance moved to the North and West is that
Europe, having a cooler climate, did not support insects all year round
as did most underdeveloped countries. Consequently, flies and
mosquitoes were not, in the northern areas, year 'round sources of
such diseases as dysentery and malaria as they were in the underdeveloped areas. Until DDT these and other insect-spread diseases
constantly drained the energy of most of what we now call underdeveloped countries.

With the introduction into European countries of Renaissance
science and mechanical technology, these nations began to improve
farming and industrial methods. Capital accumulated and soon the
areas involved were able to support more people. The relative increase of the advanced population became much greater than that of
the underdeveloped population. On the life conservation side of
Renaissance science, medicine and biology, there began to develop an
increasingly strong belief that diseases had physical causes. So, even
before Pasteur's germ theory was accepted, public health measures
were slowly improving. Small pox vaccination was being practiced
on a voluntary basis, quarantine and disease isolation laws were developing and water and sewage sanitation had been introduced. These
steps exercised considerable influence on lowering death rates from
germ-caused diseases. Since, as already mentioned, flies and mosquitoes were naturally less prevalent in these cooler climates, many of
the debilitating diseases of the underdeveloped areas were lacking or
at least less prevalent in Europe. For all these reasons the continent's
population was healthier and more vigorous than the population of
the underdeveloped countries. Europe, therefore, was a favorable

site in which modern science, agriculture, industry and medicine could and did flourish.

By the sixteenth and seventeenth centuries the world's first surplus problem had developed. Europe had developed a surplus of workers in relation to the wealth of its people as consumers. This difficulty was mitigated by exporting the surplus to North and South America, to Australia and to other colonies which the various European nations were then establishing. Unfortunately, today's surpluses can not be so easily managed.

The development of modern science meant that man had at last learned to use systematically a thought tool; a tool with which to create abstract ideas about concrete physical problems; to develop hypotheses as an intellectual challenge of the abstract ideas; and then to create techniques to physically test the hypotheses. The scientific method enabled its user to *efficiently* explore the unknown, an area previously open only to speculation. Using this marvelously efficient intellectual tool, an ever growing body of useful knowledge and ever more correct theories and principles have been developed. These have made it possible to teach people on a far larger scale than could be taught by the apprentice system. In contrast to apprentice-type education, the teaching of theories and principles can be carried out on a group basis. So scientific development made it possible to expand technical "know how" rapidly.

As we know, widespread knowledge of scientific theories and principles also proved far more effective for making useful new tools of all kinds than had the trial and error method of the earlier era. This is because the scientific method reduces the range of possible error in which it is necessary to experiment. The range of necessary experiment is defined by the hypothesis (pre-theory) being tested. If the hypothesis is a sound one, it is consonant with known facts and so trial and error (experimental tests) do not need to extend into the known areas. This permits orderly planning of a reasonable number of tests to prove or disprove the hypothesis in the unknown area.

Prior to the introduction of the scientific method (about 1450) all man's tools and inventions and improvements had been discovered on an intuitive or on an essentially accidental, trial and error, basis. This is and was the principle thought pattern of the artist and the artisan whose prime task is to *preserve the known*. Their knowledge does not rest on theory or scientific principles. It is purely empirical in nature, and is passed from generation to generation essentially by means of the apprentice system. This essentially one-teacher-to-

PHASES IN THE DEVELOPMENT OF ADVANCED COUNTRIES

PHASES	Type of public mass medicine economically possible.	Type of industrial organization (Type of energy)	General level of economic development.	Mass educational level required.
1st Phase (before the 19th Century.)	Quarantine and isolation types of public health.	Agriculture Handicraft (Solar energy stored in foods)	Very low	3 R's
2nd Phase (19th Century)	Water, sewage and food hygiene and mass vaccination (in later part of the century.)	Crude mass production (Solar energy to provide food, as well as wind and water power. Stored chemical energy in wood and coal)	Low	Beginning technical education
3rd Phase (1st half of 20th Century.)	Personal medical care, including rehabilitation, for most people. High levels of public health protection.	Advanced mass production, beginning automation (Stored chemical energy in coal and oil. Widespread electric transport.)	Moderately high	Highly specialized technical education to relatively large numbers.
4th Phase (Last half of Century.)	Personal preventive medicine, the much more expensive medicine of the future.	Automation on a general scale, perhaps coupled with cheap H-fusion energy and plastic and glass materials	Very high	True mass culture in art science and literature.

one-apprentice system of education did not permit a rapid expansion in the number of artisans, even had such an end been desired. Of course, as we know, it was not desired and the artisans' guilds were careful not to allow uncontrolled expansion of their numbers. Because of the inherent slowness of trial and error as a way of getting new knowledge, agricultural and industrial efficiency increased very slowly. Naturally, food supply also increased slowly. So a rapid expansion of the human population was an impossibility before the development of science.

Science has so speeded the rate of technical advance that time after time, in nation after nation, surpluses of things and people have developed. At the same time that science has caused these social imbalances, it has also given men a sense that they can have more control over their destiny. The result of these two factors is that the world has been suffering from bigger and bigger social revolutions and related wars. We must now, in the presence of the ultimate weapons of H-bombs and intercontinental missiles, find ways to harmonize our social organization with our scientific development in more rational ways. Violent revolutions are no longer practical or sensible ways for reorganizing modern industrial societies, and war is not even a possible way to accomplish such ends.

The preceeding table summarizes the main developments which I have been discussing. It relates the developments in industry and medicine to the factors of energy, education and standard of living.

It is, of course, impossible to separate sharply these phases or their different aspects—medicine, education, industry and economic development. But we can see by focusing on the broad outlines of history that we have passed through them. Large-scale community living was made possible by water, sewage and other forms of sanitation. Advancing industry and medicine developed specialized technical education. Specialized technical education could only be supported by a large and reasonable wealthy community, and so on. We have passed through a complex history in which agriculture, industry and medicine have been doing the equivalent of a three-man mountain-climbing act, with first one in the lead and then the other. And science has been the catalyst at every stage. We in the "advanced" countries are only now entering the fourth phase of social economic development—the phase of large-scale automation and possibly of unlimited (H-fusion) energy.

In approaching the economic problems of the underdeveloped countries, we must remember the economic importance of the more efficient rearing of children and the greater efficiency in agriculture that Pasteur's germ theory made possible for us. Modern scientific disease control was the basic factor in our rapid accumulation of surplus capital in the late nineteenth and twentieth centuries. The resulting accumulation of surplus capital permitted us to expand our schools and educate more engineers and scientists who in turn built more factories to produce more wealth. Seeing this will help us realize education is not an expense, but is the seed from which society renews itself. Increased capital wealth also made it possible to mechanize our farms, thus freeing farm workers to man the factories. Improved public health provided the engineers and scientists and workers, thousands of whom would have died in childhood, if we had not already mastered infectious disease. These engineers, scientists and workers in turn developed the machines, power sources and organization we now call automation, and they laid the foundation for the new energy revolution now beginning. We must keep these sequences in mind as we approach the problem of helping under-developed countries.

Here are some of the great strides that have occurred in the advanced areas in the brief span of 500 years:

Agriculture has moved from the man with a hoe to the tractor and combine.

Mechanics has passed from the simple water wheel to space satellites.

Chemistry has moved from the dreams of the alchemist to the actual transmutation of elements and the production of plastic substitutes superior to many of the natural things they replace.

Atomic physics has passed from mere philosophical speculations to atomic fission and H-fusion.

Energetics has passed from the stage where most men controlled little more than their own energy, to a stage where there now are only practical limits to the amount of force a man can control and to a stage where he has never-tiring, metal machines which require no calories when they are not working.

Medicine has passed from little more than witch-craft to the stage of penicillin, DDT and transplanted and artificial organs.

Can it be possible that after making such strides, we now have reached a situation where we and the Soviets cannot find a way to get science and humanity back on the track of increasing man's power over nature and improving his life? After a million years of struggle, is there no solution to our disagreements except to end it all in a nuclear holocaust, or for civilization to dissolve in an uncontrolled population growth which could flow into and insidiously destroy the advanced nations?

Chapter XII

THINGS AND PEOPLE

In this chapter we will take a closer look at more recent historical developments in the advanced countries, especially in our country. This will be done in order to see how America got into the situation where it is threatened by surpluses of things and leisure and to see how our surpluses might be usefully combined with the shortages in the underdeveloped countries.

We have seen that science moved north and west from northern Italy into Europe and from there to America. This path was followed not because of chance, but primarily because ideas flourished only in a relatively free environment—an environment which is not too strongly dedicated to preserving the status quo. Europe and later America provided such an atmosphere, because the amount of natural wealth in relation to population was high as compared with the underdeveloped areas. A third element—health—has not received much consideration as an economic factor in man's industrial growth. Most economists seem to consider it merely a by-product of increased wealth. Health is of *fundamental* importance as an economic factor, and our approach to the problems of the underdeveloped countries will be enhanced by recognizing this to be the case. I will try to show the importance of health to our own development.

Though certain steps toward improved public health had occurred prior to Pasteur, they were trivial in their effect on the general health as compared with what has followed him. In his youth, the open well and open privy were standard plumbing facilities. Public water, milk and food sanitation were unknown and disease and death were on a scale such that average life expectancy in France was about 40 years. It was not uncommon for families to have 10 or more children and to raise only 3 or 4 into adult life. Billions of years of parental effort were *invested* in children who died before they ever produced a thing. And, of course, deaths of children and adults do not tell the whole story. The billions of man-years lost through illness and invalidism, because of the inability to control infectious diseases, were another never-ending drain on the economy of that day.

We can get a measure of the economic importance of health from the following table compiled in 1951 by the late Dr. C. E. A. Winslow. This table is based on data collected before DDT and penicillin had had an appreciable effect on world health.

	Developed Areas	Intermediate Areas	Underdeveloped Areas
Proportion of world population	1/5	less than 1/6	2/3
Annual per capita income (U.S. dollars)	461	154	41
Food supply (calories per day)	3,040	2,760	2,150
Physicians per 100,000 population	106	78	17
Life expectancy (years)	63	52	30

The advanced countries in Pasteur's youth would have presented figures somewhere between those of the "Intermediate" and "Underdeveloped" areas of this table. Now, 100 years after he proved that germs could cause disease, life expectancy at birth is approximately 70 years. By 1895, when Pasteur died, he and a few other doctors and scientists throughout the world had demonstrated the bacterial causes of tuberculosis, cholera, typhoid, rabies, anthrax, childbed fever, and many other infectious diseases. Pasteur's work was already beginning to revolutionize medicine and public health and the *production and maintenance of human beings was becoming much more efficient.*

Not only did the germ theory revolutionize medicine in the advanced countries, but in reducing lost time from illness and premature deaths it also created the health foundation for the remarkable economic growth which has occurred in the past 50 to 75 years in Europe and America. The increasingly efficient productivity of modern industry has only been possible because increased efficiency in the production and conservation of human beings has kept pace at every step.

In contrast with advanced ones the persistence of high levels of disease and early death has been a continuing economic drain on underdeveloped areas. The staggering economic costs of disease and early death in the underdeveloped areas cannot even be sensibly estimated. But to get some idea of the figures involved let us look at an estimate of these costs in our own country. Even in so healthy and highly developed a nation as ours, the annual costs of preventable disease were, according to Dr. C. E. A. Winslow, as follows in 1951:

Cost of premature death	11 Billion
Cost of total disability	11 Billion
Cost of partial disability	11 Billion
Cost of short-term illness	5 Billion
Total	38 Billion

No doubt these costs have now been considerably reduced by penicillin and numerous other recent advances in medicine, but disease,
disability and premature death are still a heavy burden upon us.
However, the nature of our disease burden is changing. Infectious
diseases may now be said to be an insignificant cause of death. They
constitute less than 10% of total deaths. Degenerative disease is now
becoming the important health factor in our economy.

As we consider the matter of foreign aid it is important that we
keep this set of facts in mind. Improved living involves not only increased per capita food production and improved machines. It also
entails improved efficiency in producing and conserving people and
in educating them as well—i.e. not one or the other, but all. Let us
look at how greatly American efficiency in producing and conserving
people has increased in this century.

HEALTH CHANGES IN THE UNITED STATES (1900 TO 1950)

Item		1900	1950
Life expectancy at birth		50 years	70 years
Percent of children dying before age 21		23%	5%
Maternal deaths in childbirth		1 in 164 births	1 in 1205 births
Incidence of and deaths from surgical infections		A major hazard of surgery	An infrequent, seldom fatal complication
Mortality rates of four of the most serious contagious and infectious diseases. (Deaths per 100,000 population)	Pneumonia	202	31
	Tuberculosis	194	22
	Diptheria	40	0.3
	Typhoid Fever	31	0.1

The fact that reliable statistics do not go back further than 1900
is an indication of how deficient our public health facilities were in
pre-Pasteur times when the causes of disease were unknown. Since,
before the germ theory was proved, most people thought diseases were

a punishment of fate for evil doing, there was little cause to keep statistics on them. Diseases supposedly caused by a senseless and unpredictable fate are not likely to evoke much useful thought about how to prevent them.

In the veterinary realm, related changes have taken place. Anthrax, animal cholera and many other diseases were a constant drain on animal husbandry in our grandparents' time. The tools for preventing and curing most animal diseases today are as efficient as those used in combating human diseases. Knowledge of plant diseases, which has also grown out of Pasteur's germ theories, today prevent billions of dollars of losses for our farmers. So we have also achieved a remarkable degree of efficiency in producing food as well.

I think we can see that American civilization is the result of combining (1) a vast continent with great natural wealth, (2) a cool climate more or less unfavorable to insect diseases, and (3) a population reared in scientifically and technically advanced Europe and England which was able to adapt quickly the basic scientific knowledge in both engineering and medicine, and utilize it to produce better living and more wealth. Finally, we should note in this connection that it was fortunate that America's history began *after* the age of science was well begun. Otherwise this country might have become overpopulated with a purely agricultural based people before it could have been developed industrially. Thus it could have ended with too low a ratio of wealth to people as in India and China today. Had this happened we never could have quickly amassed the large sums of surplus capital as we did; the surplus capital which permitted us to experiment and learn the possibilities of modern mass production—America's greatest contribution to industrial progress. Nor would we have had either the capital or the freedom to install so rapidly the new techniques of modern industry and modern medicine and public health.

And now our economic productivity has become so tremendous we are seriously worried lest we have produced more things than we can consume. The 1958 recession indicated that at least temporarily production and consumption had once again gotten out of balance. But whether or not the recession becomes a depression, we can rest assured that it is madness to believe that our economy can continue to expand the manufacture of things *indefinitely*. There *must* be an upper limit to the per capita number of cars and refrigerators and television sets and the amount of beer and cigarettes that people can consume. If our productive efficiency grows faster than that appetite, the day is bound to come, sooner or later, when the public says, "I'm stuffed. I can't consume another morsel." It is a finite world and it is absurd to base our economy almost entirely on a belief that Americans have an *infinite* appetite for things. Today, when most products of our economy are consumed in this country, Americans constitute 170 million people. There are approximately 10 times as many underdeveloped people. It seems to me that rather than consider our surpluses as a threat to us we should count them as a blessing, and figure out how to expand into that market. Instead of "Buy American" our slogan should be "Sell to the Underdeveloped." Our surpluses can provide us with the wherewithal to help the underdeveloped areas and, as I will show in a subsequent chapter, thereby create a world of truly peaceful United Nations.

If the above analysis of our economic development is correct it leads to these conclusions of importance to a consideration of foreign aid:

1. We who were born in the advanced areas were awfully lucky. We had the good luck of living in rich and relatively thinly populated areas, and also the good luck of having a relatively healthy climate. Our "boot strap" transformation from an agricultural into an industrial society was only possible because all these "lucky" factors were present.

2. The underdeveloped countries have been caught in a vicious cycle of overpopulation, limited natural wealth, and excessive disease and death rates. They cannot follow our path to economic development because of this.

3. If the underdeveloped areas are to escape the vicious cycle they are in they must have outside help.

To see the problems of developing the underdeveloped nations in proper perspective we should recall the population chart shown in the previous chapter. It took a million years for the human population to reach a total of about 250 million at the time of Christ, an average increase of only 250 people per year for that first million years. In the 1,895 years which elapsed between the birth of Christ and the death of Pasteur world population increased to 1600 million. That was still an increase of less than a million a year. Since the nations of the advanced part of the world still had unsettled virgin soil, this expansion did not create any wide-spread population pressures and the resulting social changes, even in a long life, were not too remarkable. However, in the period 1895 to 1950, world population increased from 1600 million to 2400 million, an average annual increase of 15 million and at the present time the average increase is in excess of 25 million per year. When we place these figures in proper perspective as the graph does and relate the curves to the highly optimistic estimate of 16 billion as the absolute population ceiling for the world, we see what looks like an irresistible force heading toward an immovable object. Unless we can find a humane and politically feasible way to bring births and deaths into a world balance so population numbers will reach a stationary figure civilization and human culture is surely doomed by these circumstances.

There is no easy way out of it. The world contains a fixed amount of land and this is the way it was being used in 1952:

CATEGORY	PERCENT OF TOTAL	POSSIBLE USE FOR FOOD AND FIBER PRODUCTION
Desert and Wasteland	23.3	
Built on	14.6	Impossible
	37.9	
Pasture and meadow	19.5	
Crop land	9.2	Now in use for food and
Orchards and Gardens	0.5	fiber production.
Accessible forest	8.5	
	37.7	
Inaccessible forest	21.1	Potential reserve but
Unused	3.3	no doubt very expensive
	24.4	to develop.
Total	100.0	

Even if we could learn to use all the inaccessible and unused land of the world, we could not double our present amount of land for growth of food and fiber. But 16 billion people is 6 times as many as are now in the world. In the absence of some sane and civilized action to bring all the world to advanced status and then to find a means to achieve a birth/death balance, it can clearly be foreseen that the time will arrive when billions of ignorant, illiterate, starving humans will swarm over our cities (the cultural nuclei of our civilization) and destroy them. It is pointless in this context to discuss the possible techniques, ranging from prayers to pills, which have been suggested to accomplish control. In the present state of cold war competition it is unthinkable that anything important can be done to head off this eventuality. Too many national rivalries are encouraging population increases for strategic reasons.

A humane and democratic solution to the population problem will only be possible in a peaceful world in which most people are literate, reasonably knowledgeable and psychologically sound individuals. It can be stated without fear of refutation that: *Unless a world population policy can be adopted soon enough to prevent world population from exceeding 16 billion (at most), it is certain that hungry masses of people will overrun all efforts at government and drive humanity into the most intolerable conditions ever encountered on this earth by any form of animal life.*

It is one thing to have a breakdown of central authority in an essentially agricultural economy. This is the state in which Egyptian and Chinese life had existed for several hundred years after breakdown of their earlier dynasties until in recent years they both began to reestablish a central governmental organization. Under those conditions of rural living their populations were able to eke out a hand to mouth existence for generations. But, let an industrial society such as ours, whose members are mostly living in cities separated from the land, break down; let the trains stop running and the distribution system cease operating; let the hungry city people then reverse the tide and overrun and plunder the countryside. What then? The way of life of cannibal tribes would seem idyllic by comparison with what overpopulation on the present potential scale and under the present economic conditions would mean.

In subsequent chapters I will show how the underdeveloped areas offer an arena in which the advanced countries could compete peacefully with each other. I believe we have the opportunity to combine their shortages and our surpluses in a way that will be of great advantage to all of us as well as profitable for American business.

CHAPTER XIII

WEALTH IS ENERGY

Wealth is not dollars or pounds or francs or rubles. It is energy and the power to control energy. The caveman who controlled only his own energy was a poor man, indeed. He needed at least 3000 or 4000 calories of energy a day just for his own existence, and his wife and children required equivalent amounts. He had only his hands to procure it, and no means to store it for any but the shortest periods of time. Small wonder that man has taken a long time to accumulate any appreciable amount of surplus energy—capital—with which to take the steps into industrialization.

When man developed his first weapons and tools, he increased his efficiency in hunting and agriculture; he became more efficient in taking *calories of energy* from nature. With that increase in efficiency, he then had more time to make more and better tools. However since he could make only *hand* tools and since there was small advantage in having two sets of tools for one set of hands, man's progress in accumulating wealth was more or less hung up at this stage for a long time.

But then he learned to domesticate animals. Since men could either milk or ride or eat these animals, he had a new source of natural energy at his command and his wealth began to grow again. The next stage was to acquire slaves who provided extra hands to use the extra sets of tools. But slaves are only profitable if they produce more calories than they consume. Since slave babies couldn't work and disease often killed them, they had serious limitations as energy machines. Slowly over centuries man succeeded in replacing living machines with cheaper, more economical and more efficient metal ones.

If we take the total calories used in America per day and divide it by the number of people in this country—170 million—we get the figure 160,000. So we may say the average American is rich enough to spend 160,000 calories of energy every day. If we divide 160,000 by the daily energy expenditure (4000 calories) of the average caveman it turns out that we are 40 times as rich. Actually, because of our greater efficiency in the use and conservation of our available energy we greatly exceed this figure.

Gradually as man's social development progressed he began to develop techniques for learning more about the forces of nature and to invent machines to use those forces—first, machines which used water and wind, and, later, fire to energize steam engines. Eventually man learned to use the stored chemical energy of coal and oil. Now he has at last even learned to tap the ultimate energy of the atom itself.

In 1945, we entered the atomic energy age and in 1955 we used atomic power for the first time to do useful work—to drive a submarine. With the 1957 announcement of controlled H-fusion, as yet only on a laboratory scale, we seem to be on the verge of an energy revolution that will make nonsense of all previous economic values. For H-fusion presents the prospect of an engine which could yield more energy than it consumes. It would be almost the energy equivalent of perpetual motion. Such an engine is still at least a few years away and cannot be guaranteed. But physicists are clearly optimistic that useful H-fusion energy is coming. Man's previous advance has been on the basis of slow, step-by-step increases in mechanical and biological efficiency. But H-fusion energy would produce a quantum jump in our available energy. This would have the effect of making past rates of economic advance appear to have been at a snail's pace.

The rapid technical progress we made in the industrial age was not accomplished because we had become much more efficient in using energy. The most efficient gasoline engine is still not so efficient as the human body and wastes a great deal of the fuel consumed as unwanted heat. As we shifted from wood to coal to oil, we did not appreciably increase fuel efficiency. Oil does not provide much more energy than coal, nor coal than wood, on a pound-for-pound basis. The one factor in this economic area that has been improving, and that most accounts for our technical progress, is improved skill and efficiency in transporting energy. We have developed a vast energy distribution system and great skill in operating the system. Water power is tied to a river. Steam power must stay close to coal or wood sources. The machines using coal and wood as fuel must necessarily be heavy. But oil and gasoline can be cheaply pumped through pipes and carried easily in tanks, and then be burned in small amounts in relatively light-weight machines. Electric energy can also be transported over considerable distances with relatively little energy loss. Thus, the nature of liquid fuels and of electricity has made it possible for us to transport energy to the raw material sources and save a great deal of useless hauling.

These factors in the transportation and use of energy have been at the bottom of our increased industrial efficiency. But while these energy developments have been going on, we have been depleting the world's resources both of raw materials and of stored chemical energy —wood, coal and oil. So, as use techniques improved, the fuels to energize the better machines have been growing gradually more scarce. The day can now be foreseen when the oil and coal of the world *will be gone*. At *present use rates,* their complete exhaustion would probably occur within 250 years at least. Our reserves of metals and other natural resources have also been diminishing. But now science has escaped this dead end.

The controlled release of atomic energy from the heavy element, uranium, the basis of the power of the atomic submarine, took us into the realm of atomic-energized machines for the first time, and provides for a coal and oil substitute. But the gain in overall efficiency as compared with oil and coal is not so great, because uranium, and the other elements which can be used in this way are rare. Hence the cost of mining, transporting and refining the huge quantities of ores needed to obtain these rare elements is relatively high. And even more important in the production cost of A-energy, is the greater capital investment needed in the power plants compared with the cost of plants for extracting energy from coal or oil. And like oil and coal, there is only a limited and ever-diminishing amount of these heavy elements which can be used this way. So the more we use, the more expensive the basic fuels would eventually become. However, compared with coal and oil reserves, these heavy element reserves are large (probably enough for several thousand years) and, of course, the transportation efficiency of atomic as compared with chemical fuel could hardly be greater.

If useful hydrogen fusion energy becomes a reality in the next few years, the energy revolution will enter an even more remarkable phase. There is enough (heavy) hydrogen in the oceans to serve as H-fusion fuel for foreseeable power needs for billions of years ahead. The economic effect of such a development would probably be that in the future the use of chemical energy in the form of coal, gas and wood would cease. They would be replaced for most industrial purposes by atomic energy and probably would be reserved for limited uses in which atomic energy would always be impractical. Under these conditions, the oil-bearing real estate of Arabia, Venezuela and other countries would quickly lose its value as a source of immediate wealth.

In similar fashion, the development of numerous forms of plastics and of industrial glass which can be substituted for metals, and the discovery of ways of extracting magnesium from the ocean may have the effect of reducing the relative value of many metals such as iron, copper, and aluminum. This may happen even though the world reserves of metals constantly grow smaller. Such a development could also have effects on "real-estate" values. Certainly these developments tend to reduce the strategic importance of these metals. The situation brings to mind the rubber situation in World War II. When we were cut off from natural rubber we developed a chemical substitute and so ceased to be strategically dependent on natural rubber. The strategic and also the actual value of rubber plantations was thereby greatly reduced. The present cold war strategy of both sides is based on "real estate" values which may soon be historically outmoded.

As the result of the energy and matter revolutions, it seems certain that our internal economic values will also shift in the next few years. While oil, steel, coal and copper may never completely lose their value, relatively speaking, the "matter" future is with plastics and other synthetics produced by chemistry just as the energy future is certainly with atomic power. Our planning for the future and particularly our strategic planning should reckon with this matter and energy revolution.

But we not only have surplus products and energy to worry us. We also have surplus time—leisure—to deal with.

The number of hours in the work week has been steadily declining and producing a growing amount of leisure. In order to study the changes in the leisure situation I have made some calculations of the percentage of total life time spent at work and in leisure at three different time periods in history. The estimates are for American men whose lives did (or will) center at the years shown in the following table.

Percent of average life-time spent in	Mid-point of different average lives		
	1885	1950	2000
Work	26.0	15.3	7.9
Leisure	7.8	20.7	27.1

Americans already have a great deal of leisure and are heading toward still more. But at the very time we seem to have surpluses of leisure, matter and energy, the underdeveloped two-thirds of the world is hungering for things and energy and no doubt longing for a little leisure also. In the long run these countries also pose a threat to our well-being.

Are we Americans smart enough to make a business deal out of this situation, to direct our human and material resources to new tasks, to pair shortage in the underdeveloped areas with our excess bounty and make the combination pay off for both parties? I think we can. But if we are to succeed, we must use imagination and look at many things in new ways.

First, we must recognize that basic scientists, the people with the "know how"—the ideas—to manipulate the forces of nature, are at least as valuable and as exportable as things and energy itself. We must learn to "sell" ideas as effectively as we have sold things and services. When the people of this country realize that this kind of business leads to peace and away from war, they will suppport it. We already have the experienced business men who could organize and finance the operation. We have a large supply of well-trained scientists of all kinds who have the "know-how" and the capacity to produce ideas. All we need is to combine the two groups into a saleable "package."

But the cold war policies of both this country and the U.S.S.R. are still the "real-estate" minded, and energy shortage policies of a period of history which seems to be rapidly drawing to a close. If we cannot shift our thinking and planning to keep pace with the future, and if we continue to make long range plans on the basis of values which daily grow more obsolete, we invite defeat of our strategy.

Chapter XIV

DDT AND INSECT-SPREAD DISEASE

While the advanced countries have been developing an ever higher standard of living over the past few centuries and especially in the past 50 or 75 years, what has been happening in North Africa, Egypt, Afghanistan, India, Burma, Indonesia and all the other underdeveloped countries?

As a generalization we may say that until World War II most of these countries had been existing in the same dark age from which Europe escaped in the Renaissance. Disease and poverty, despair, misery and early death had for centuries been the fate of all but a few of those living in the underdeveloped countries. Then, in the midst of World War II, a remarkable new factor entered the scene, a factor of revolutionary proportions—the insect killer, DDT. It suddenly prevented much of the disease and early death in those countries. DDT is a health force capable of accomplishing in the underdeveloped countries what Pasteur's germ theory did in the advanced ones. In fact, it is already doing it and much faster, and therein lies the revolutionary aspect of this problem. The result has been the stopping of disease and death. But this only adds to the total misery and hunger, when the food supply is as limited as it is in most of these countries.

Suddenly millions of people have been given a greatly improved level of health. Millions and millions of people who, were it not for DDT, would now be dead or at best existing in an apathetic state of malaria-induced anemia, are now alive and clamoring for more food. Their new vigor has given urgency to the political demands of their leaders. Many Americans think these strong demands are the result of Soviet propaganda, when, in fact, they actually derive from American introduced DDT. This strategic misconception is a dramatic illustration of the penalty for not having science adequately represented in the upper echelons of government. Our political leaders have not understood the basic roots of the problem they faced.

It will be useful to digress at this point to consider in some detail the important differences in climate and disease between the advanced and underdeveloped countres. Why during the past 100 years has

114

public health failed to improve in the underdeveloped countries while at the same time it has improved so rapidly in advanced countries? Some think the advanced people were healthier because they were from "better stock," or because they were "naturally" more sanitary and so on. It seems far more likely that the advanced peoples have been healthier because they lived in better climates and had less severe disease problems to harrass them than did those who lived in the generally warmer, moister, tropical and subtropical areas. In the latter areas *insect-spread germ and parasite* diseases in addition to the respiratory spread and food and water-borne diseases common to both areas were prevalent on a year-'round basis. In the cooler, advanced countries, insects (especially mosquitoes and flies) are generally dormant in the winter, and in the higher regions of these countries insects do not even thrive in summer. Hence, people in these cooler areas have, by comparison, been more or less been spared the insect-borne diseases. This gave the people in cooler climates a health advantage. But until Pasteur, the people in advanced countries suffered frequently from devastating epidemics, usually water or food borne or respiratory-spread germ diseases—epidemics which time after time slowed their forward progress. So until Pasteur the health differences between advanced and underdeveloped countries were not so great. We had one general group of diseases, they had two. Then with the proof that many of our most prevalent diseases were caused by germs, and the subsequent development of ways to cure or prevent them, the advanced regions gained a second and tremendous health advantage over the underdeveloped lands. We then began to get rid of our one group of diseases, and now have actually reached the stage where germs have become a minor cause of death. Naturally, the germ theory has done less for public health in underdeveloped areas where insect-borne diseases were so important as they were in Africa, Southern Asia and South America. These areas were even too poor to "buy" modern methods for sanitary handling of water, sewage and food. They could not afford to take the logical steps indicated by the germ theory.

Most germ diseases are acute in nature. They occur and the patient either recovers fully or he dies quickly. Not so with many tropical diseases, especially malaria. Many, many victims live for years in an apathetic, debilitated, anemic state. Many foreigners have mistakenly considered this lethargy to be due to "innate laziness." Dr. Paul Russell, world famous malariologist, was one of the first to contrast the apathetic, dispirited, quiet children he had observed in Sardinia, when malaria was prevalent there, with the healthy, happy, noisy youngsters he saw after the island had been freed of malaria.

Now let us consider the story of DDT and its influence on history. In 1944 our soldiers and those of our allies were stationed in many of the underdeveloped countries of the world, and in most of them mosquito-borne malaria was the number one disease threat to the soldiers. Thanks to the medical foresight of Colonel William S. Stone, our troops had a good weapon by then to combat malaria and several other insect diseases as well. The weapon was DDT *and the "know-how" to use it properly*. The full potential of this marvelous insecticide had only been discovered two years earlier by research workers of the U. S. Department of Agriculture. The discovery was made in the course of an extensive survey of all known insecticides; a survey undertaken in order to determine which of many chemicals would be the most useful for killing mosquitoes and lice under war conditions.

The search had been suggested by Colonel Stone who in 1942 was in the office of the Surgeon General, U. S. Army. Knowing the epidemiology of these and other insect-borne diseases, he drew up a set of specifications for an "ideal insecticide" to guide the surveyors in screening the hundreds of known and potential insecticides. Within a few months, in Oct. 1942, the surveyors discovered a Swiss product, DDT. Further research showed it to have far greater potential as an insecticide than had been realized by its Swiss producers.

By late 1943 Colonel Stone was in North Africa. There he and Dr. Fred Soper, world-famed tropical disease expert then on loan to the Army from the Rockefeller Foundation, planned the anti-typhus campaign which, using DDT, smothered a typhus epidemic for the first time in all history—the outbreak which occurred in Naples during the war-winter of 1943-'44.

The Naples typhus episode was not entirely over when DDT got its second big test, this time to kill malaria mosquitoes on the Anzio beach-head. On January 22, 1944, our troops landed on Anzio, where they were soon surrounded not only by Germans with their 88's but also by swamps which with the warmth of spring, were traditionally hospitable to the Anopheles mosquito. In addition, thousands of water-filled shell holes and the disruption of the normal drainage system resulting from the continuing battle of Anzio, set the stage for a spring malaria epidemic which would (in pre-DDT times) have forced our troops to withdraw. Because of the malaria hazard the Anzio assault could only have been tried in winter. It was tried only because it was assumed that the Germans would quickly be pushed back, allowing our troops to move to high ground. But this did not happen and our soldiers were forced to dig in and survive in the malarious swamps.

However, while Dr. Soper and his team of biological researchers had been perfecting the use of DDT as a weapon against louse-borne typhus, other biological scientists were studying its use as a weapon against mosquito-borne malaria. Malaria-control teams under Lt. Col. Justin Andrews were developing and learning the most efficient ways to spray DDT on mosquito breeding swamps and on their resting sites in buildings. These teams were also training prisoners of war and Italian laborers in the use of older methods of malaria control, such as swamp drainage. At the same time air-plane dusting equipment and methods was being developed by the Air Force. By spring-time when the malaria season began at Anzio, the counter offensive with DDT and other anti-malaria weapons was ready. It proved to be as successful as the anti-typhus campaign in Naples and our troops were able to survive until they became strong enough to break the German encirclement and resume the attack. Without DDT, this military feat would have been unthinkable.

In the ensuing campaign ending in the capture of Rome, DDT enabled the allies to fight through the Pontine marshes without being decimated by malaria as previous armies had been. Thus Rome was captured from the South for the first time in history.

DDT played an equally decisive role in the war in the Pacific. Many readers will remember how the first divisions to reach Guadal-canal were quickly destroyed as fighting units—not by the Japanese, but by malaria. Many of these divisions had to be withdrawn from battle after only a few weeks because they were so weakened by the disease. They were sent to Australia, where they were slowly nursed back to health and fighting strength only after months of expert medical care. After DDT was introduced, malaria, diarrhea, dysentery and other insect-borne diseases, which until then had been allies of the Japanese, were forced to switch sides. Malaria mosqui-toes then became "microscopic allies" of MacArthur, and his troop strength was no longer seriously reduced by them.

The Japanese, by comparison with us *after we had DDT*, were at a great disadvantage. They continued to suffer high morbidity throughout the war not only for want of DDT, but because they lacked other modern health weapons (notably penicillin) which biological research had given us.

The biological and medical sciences won many other dramatic battles in the war. Like the DDT story, the penicillin story was also based on biological research. Penicillin and other antibiotics and the great knowledge and skill of our scientists, physicians and surgeons were responsible for the remarkably low rates of disease and high rates of salvage among our sick and wounded and the consequent high morale and fighting strength of our troops. Our efficient manipulation of biological tools made it possible for a relatively small number of men to exert a tremendous military force in areas of the world where disease had always before seriously weakened or destroyed such efforts.

Perhaps the most remarkable biological victory during the World War II period was the postwar victory over typhus. Not only was there no epidemic of typhus after World War II, there was not even a large-scale outbreak—only scattered localized ones. To appreciate the meaning of that sentence it is necessary to know that after World War I more than 25 million Europeans were stricken with typhus and several million died. It was typhus that created much of the economic and political choas that followed that earlier war. The typhus epidemic which did *not* occur in Europe after World War II was one of the most dramatic chapters in the history of preventive medicine.

The DDT anti-malaria program in the battle area was matched by related developments in the rear areas behind the battlelines. Here the programs were conducted under the auspices of Military Government and supervised by Colonel Paul Russell, Rockefeller Foundation expert on loan to the Army. For a short time in the summer of 1944 Dr. Soper also participated in this work, but his services were soon requested by the British Government to combat a malaria epidemic in Egypt which was coming down from the upper reaches of the Nile. After quickly stopping this outbreak, Dr. Soper went on to work with the British on the malaria problem in Cyprus, and with the French in combating malaria on Sardinia. Both of these formerly heavily-infested islands are now free of malaria. It was these experiences which first led Soper, now head of the Pan American Sanitation Bureau, to seriously propose eradicating malaria from large areas of the world and even to suggest that eventually the entire world could be freed of malaria. A UN sponsored program is now under way to do just that.)

Since World War II, we have spent $400 billion on the weapons of death, most of which are now obsolete. In contrast to this, relatively cheap biological tools—DDT, penicillin, etc.—have been continuously at work in ever widening areas of the world, bringing about astonishing health and population changes, especially in the so-called underdeveloped or "have-not" countries.

These public health measures have suddenly brought health improvements comparable to those we have made gradually over a period of 75 years or so. Such sudden and radical health changes have had great social consequences. To fully comprehend the social effect of DDT and antibiotics in the underdeveloped countries, it is necessary to recall the already discussed fundamental disease and health differences between the advanced countries and the underdeveloped ones, resulting in the fact that the advanced countries have been much healthier than the underdeveloped ones and so their people have lived longer, more productive and more economically efficient lives. When the average life span is from 20 to 30 years there is little time or money for education— the basic factor that improves agriculture and industry and raises living standards. Underdeveloped countries and their people have been in an extremely vicious cycle.

Now with DDT and antibiotics, health standards in the underdeveloped areas are such that these people are on the way to catching up with us in life expectancy. Death rates and disease rates are falling faster than they ever fell in the United States or Europe. The rate at which the life span is now increasing in the underdeveloped areas has never been equalled in human history. The resulting population is undoubtedly a revolutionary force of first magnitude in the politics of the Middle and Far East, and in all the underdeveloped areas of the world. Nationalism and the urgency of the leaders of these areas is certainly a reflection of people clamoring for a better life. They are suddenly, in their newly gained health and vigor, extremely vocal. We might say that hemoglobin has become a political force of major proportions.

It is ironical that when, in 1944, Churchill's Government invited Soper to introduce DDT into Cyprus and the Nile Valley it may inadvertently have hastened the liquidation of the British Empire. The level of health in both these and other areas has risen rapidly since then. With their new-found energy these people have emphatically rejected British as well as other colonial rulers.

Headlines usually deal only with the open manifestation of these power struggles. They often ignore the fundamental changes beneath the surface events. For this reason DDT, penicillin, and other biological tools which have produced many small "miracles" have been overlooked as political forces. Let us look at some examples:

In Afghanistan, the price of land before malaria control was Afghanis 300 per acre. After malaria control, the value in the same district increased to Afghanis 5,000 to 8,000.

In Thailand with malaria mosquitoes at the point of disappearance in formerly highly malarious areas, it has been estimated that the anti-malaria program costing a half-million dollars a year, will increase rice yields by $15 million.

In India, formerly one of the most malarious countries of the world, according to a statement by Dr. Soper in 1955, "by tactics equivalent to eradication, 100,000,000 persons are now protected . . . still leaving 200,000,000 to go."

In Ceylon, out of 8 million people, 70,000 people died of malaria in 1935. Today in the settled areas the disease has been brought under 100 percent control. Food production and other agricultural pursuits were unpopular prior to 1946. But since malaria has been controlled, there is "land hunger" among the people and the government is unable to meet the demands for more land for agricultural pursuits.

In Greece, malaria control in a single year since World War II augmented the labor effort by 30,000,000 man days. Before the war, there were between 1 and 2 million cases of malaria annually. In 1952 there were 408 cases.

In Italy, malaria is now practically eradicated. In 1955 there were only 5 cases, whereas in 1945 there were 400,000 cases.

In Burma and Pakistan, rice production increased by 15 percent in the first year after malaria was controlled in certain areas.

In Iran, after malaria was controlled, the rice crop was harvested by 4 laborers per hectare, whereas formerly 10 were needed for the same production.

In Indonesia, over 12,000 acres of land in East Java, which had been abandoned because of malaria, were returned to rice production after malaria control.

Perhaps the most remarkable aspect of these examples is this: To a large extent they were made possible by American scientific and medical research. Millions of people living in these countries right now owe their very lives to DDT and penicillin and other products of American science, medicine and industry. Yet many of these people are distrustful of us and some of them even hate us. Something is surely wrong in such a situation. We can blame these attitudes entirely on anti-American propaganda and on human perverseness. But I think we should largely blame the situation on our own failure, first to understand what we have accomplished, and then to follow through with the other biological tools which should logically have followed the public health miracles we made possible.

Instead of belaboring Nasser, Nehru, Sukarno and others, we should realize that the population pressures that we played such a major role in creating, have enormously complicated the transition from a colonial to a free status. Their relatively weak and inexperienced governments face biological problems of staggering proportions. We, who possess the largest and finest group of biologists in the world, have failed in the post-war years to use them with the effectiveness their skills deserve and the problems demand. Because our leaders have not understood the forces of biology, they have not even been aware of the source and strength of the popular pressures with which most political leaders in the underdeveloped areas have had to deal. We have blamed them for being politicians—for responding to and reflecting the popular pressures on them. Nothing can be more politically sterile than blaming a politician for responding to popular pressures of such force.

We have failed to appreciate that medicine and biology are potent social-political forces. So far preventive medicine has merely raised hemoglobin levels—raised the appetites and vigor of these people we have been describing. But appetite in the absence of food is hunger. We must follow through with programs to help these people channel their increased vigor into a more satisfying kind of life. Our peace time leaders have not shown the wisdom our medical people demonstrated in meeting the biological problems of war. It is not too late, but the political sands are flowing fast these days.

CHAPTER XV

BIOLOGY: NEGLECTED TOOL OF DIPLOMACY

Unhappily, our peaceful scientific tools have been given far less publicity than our A-bombs and H-bombs. Our government, our educational institutions, and industry have too often failed to recognize and applaud the outstanding work done by our own biological scientists. The story of DDT told in the previous chapter is an example of this neglect. The Swiss chemist who first discovered the insecticide properties of DDT but who did not realize its public health potential received a Nobel prize. But essentially nothing has been done to honor the Americans whose brilliant development of DDT as a public health tool really brought it to the attention of the world.

This is one of many examples of our failure to recognize the role of the biologists and their importance to our well-being. A more recent one is the fact that among cooperating nations for the International Geophysical Year, the United States was the only nation with no organized biological program. We vote billions for the development of scientific weapons of death. We honor the men who help us make them, even when we know some of them not many years ago were developing weapons to destroy us. But we give little recognition to the scientists who work on the weapons to destroy disease and extend our own lives. How can we hope to convince the world of our peaceful desires when we do such a poor job of recognizing the peaceful, lifegiving discoveries of our own scientists?

The development of a policy of "peaceful competition" outlined here may not only divert the cold war into constructive, peaceful channels, but it can also do much to restore science to a favored position with our young people. It would help to substitute in the minds of our youngsters the feeling that the high adventure of life instead of the threat of atomic death was the main business of science.

Our failure to use biology in diplomacy led me to suggest in an earlier chapter that we bring scientists of all kinds, biological as well as physical, into the policy making levels of government. The United States has the biological tools to shape a new and positive foreign policy—a policy whose ultimate objective would be the attainment

122

of World Peace through the elimination of disease, ignorance and poverty everywhere in the world. But we must bring the scientists into the planning level if we want the job done. If the knowledge, skill, and resources in the advanced areas of the world, especially in America, were mobilized for this purpose, the "have-not" nations could become the kind of neighbors we want. In the remaining years of this century, a great deal could be accomplished, especially if this country and the U.S.S.R. were in peaceful (UN refereed) competition with each other to do the job.

There are many factors to be considered besides death rates in the underdeveloped countries. The population explosion figures given in the previous chapter, remarkable as they are, do not begin to tell the whole story. They ignore the psychological impact of these biological events. When supersitious people see that disease can be eliminated almost overnight by the application of DDT powder or spray or by the injection of a medicine, they have to change their beliefs about disease being the punishment of fate or of an angry god. Thus the very foundation of superstitious beliefs, which 'enthrall many, are being destroyed by these biological agents. Sick, miserable people may merely sit and contemplate a future heaven. Healthy but hungry ones bestir themselves. The story of many recent national awakenings is implicit in these equations: (1) Live mosquitoes in swamps=Malaria-apathy-resignation. (2) Live mosquitoes plus DDT=Dead mosquitoes and no malaria, energy, the will and strength to act.

True religion based on belief in the brotherhood and spiritual unity of men will not suffer from these developments. Only the darkly superstitious, basically inhuman beliefs that still influence the lives of hundreds of millions in this world will lose their strangle-hold. These negative forces are now giving way before the pressure of improved health and vigor. Passivity is being replaced by activity. Superstition and fear are giving way to confidence among these people that they can do somethng about their own futures.

Our founding fathers had this same kind of belief in their ability to direct their own lives. Our country's rapid development was based on individual self-confidence that rested on the great physical vigor which, in turn, stemmed from the generally-healthy climate and environment in which our forefathers lived. A similar self-esteem is growing in the minds of millions throughout the world. It will produce important political and economic results.

We have had a foreign aid or mutual security program since the

end of World War II, but it has too largely been dominated by a
Lady Bountiful philosophy, coupled with a "practical" interest in trying to reduce our own farm surpluses. As a result we have thought
of the people of these underdeveloped areas as "poor" people. Like
Lady Bountiful, convinced that the "poor will always be with us,"
we have believed we could not do much to help them end their
poverty. (We have forgotten how few of us had rich ancestors.)
At the same time, our conscience made us want to do *something*.
Since we had huge surpluses threatening to undermine our farm market, it was relatively painless to be "Good Samaritans" and give
away our unwanted surplus goods.

So, up to this point, a considerable part of our foreign economic
aid has actually been in the form of surpluses of food. Such aid has
little long-range economic value for those who get it. In fact, like
DDT, it often tends to aggravate the problem when there is no fol-
low-through with other programs. If these people are to overcome
their poverty, they must learn how to support themselves. During
these past few years, if we had exported "know-how" on an adequate
scale to the underdeveloped countries of the world, we could already
have strengthened the economies of these areas. Continuing technical guidance would have helped them increase their agricultural output, and develop more modern educational and technical programs.

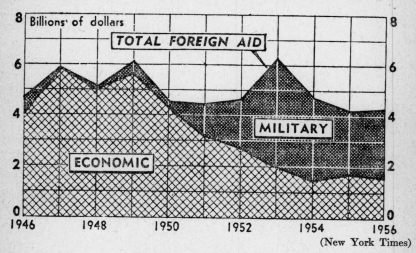

(New York Times)

They could have taken steps to reduce the terrible calory and educational and technical gaps that exist among their people. We could
thus have been assisting them in building an economy and a society

that *they* would feel was worth defending. At the same time, we would have enhanced our prestige and won many friends among them. We would also have made a substantial contribution to world peace.

Since World War II we have spent about $400 billion for arms and military power and less than $40 billion for economic assistance. Since a dollar spent for biology produces so much more than a dollar spent for weapons, this ratio might not have been too bad had we continued to give economic assistance the emphasis justified by the facts I have presented. However, economic forms of assistance have been falling off greatly since 1949 while military assistance was increased.

With so much historical evidence pointing to the strategic importance of biology, it is surprising to see the emphasis we have placed on negative military aid rather than on the positive aid of American medical, agricultural, educational and industrial "know-how." It is evident that the Soviets are becoming increasingly alert to the potentialities of biology. We must move fast if we hope to play a major role in the development of the underdeveloped.

If we adopt an all-out policy of improving the health, educational and economic conditions of the underdeveloped areas, some will fear

PERCENTAGE DECLINE OF CRUDE DEATH RATES IN 18 UNDER-DEVELOPED COUNTRIES

Periods	Number Countries Compared	Average Percent Decline From Previous Period
Half-Decade Changes		
1920-24	—	—
1925-29	15	6.0
1930-34	16	4.6
1935-39	18	6.3
1940-44	16	8.5
1945-49	16	15.2
1950-54	18	20.1
30-Year Change		
1920-24	—	—
1950-54	15	53.1

that it would create a problem of world over-population. They think better health, more food, better education and eventual industrialization will aggravate the wild population growth now going on in these nations and further increase world tensions.

Accurate statistics in the underdeveloped areas have not been widely available, but a recent population survey of the entire world made by demographer Kingsley Davis shows that a remarkable decline in the death rate in 18 underdeveloped countries occurred between the period 1940-44 and the period 1945-49. (See table on page 125).

The rate of decline in death rates which had been more or less steady for many years suddenly doubled when DDT was introduced to these countries. People stopped dying in unprecedentedly large numbers.

The short-term effect of DDT and other biological tools in underdeveloped areas has been to decrease the death rate more rapidly than the rate of productivity has increased—thus widening the calory gap in many instances. But economic and social progress rests on a complex in which public health, education, improved agriculture and modern industrialization all play a role. DDT alone is not enough, surplus food is not enough, machinery is not enough. What is required for rapid progress, is a composite program that integrates all these elements into a balanced, properly timed, and coordinated total program.

The long-term experience of the advanced countries indicates that industrialization carries its own built-in population controls. The data from the study by Kingsley Davis demonstrates this point:

POPULATION GROWTH 1800-1955

Types of Countries	Percent gain during previous 20 years							
	1820	1840	1860	1880	1900	1920	1944	1955
European	23.1	17.2	19.7	18.1	19.9	18.0	14.1	11.6
New World				64.5	47.2	48.2	30.2	32.6
Underdeveloped								37.4

The rate of population growth in European countries declined more or less continuously over the past 100 years while industrialization has gone on.

A similar and more rapid rate of decline, though at a higher level of growth, has taken place in the New World. The "New World" in this study means North, Central and South America—and so a good many people from underdeveloped countries of Central and South America are included and account for the higher level of growth. When the United States was a relatively underdeveloped agricultural nation, as it was until after the Civil War, families averaged more children than now. As industries developed and more people moved to cities, the average number of children per family decreased. This social adjustment in family size was achieved without any organized effort. It was simply impossible for parents in cities to rear and educate large families, for there was not enough money to house and clothe them, not enough living space and not enough parental energy to devote to so many children. Country children were economic assets to the family quite early in life. City children seldom become economic assets at all. When they become economically self-sufficient they usually establish their own homes. So, city life created this additional condition which encourages fewer births. With the concurrent decline in infant mortality, the fear of being left childless if one had only two or three children disappeared. The urge for large families as insurance against no survivors therefore declined.

Our history strongly suggests that if the "have-not" areas attain a way of life comparable to that in the advanced countries, they will not want to see it destroyed either from within by overpopulation or from without by other forces. It is likely that they will then control their birth rates for *their* own reasons, that is, to protect a way of life that is worth protecting.

Modern technology has made the natural population checks of famine and pestilence and war either obsolete or impractical as population controls. War has become too total to use for any purpose. DDT and other tools of modern medicine have gone far to make disease an outmoded form of population control as well. But famine and starvation are not outdated and never will be.

Population pressures can grow to uncontrollable proportions and produce unpredictable results unless we help these countries build modern societies capable of meeting these and other social problems rationally. This country, which still has leadership in the biological area, must use its power to strengthen our moral leadership in the family of nations by promoting "peaceful competition" and taking leadership in a vast program of social rehabilitation to bring the underdeveloped areas into the twentieth century space-age.

What will be the cost of such a program? The costs of education in public health and improved agricultural and industrial methods depend a good deal on how wise and efficient the operation is. In backward countries, the *early* economic dividends from this kind of education are tremendous. Once the major problems have been solved, further improvement will be relatively more costly. Consequently, the equation must continuously weigh the costs against the value of the potential results.

If the underdeveloped peoples can convert ideas into wealth as we did, there is certain to be a long-range profit. The immediate costs to us of such a program should be a secondary consideration, since we have no real alternative to adopting it. We should look at the costs of this program as we look at costs in a war. We spend what it takes to win the war in the quickest possible time.

In our biological aid program, we would spend to achieve peace by helping create a world sufficiently stable economically, socially and politically so underdeveloped countries will no longer exist as power-vacuums attracting outside intervention. This is the short-range goal. If the way of life of the *advanced* people of the world would eventually be destroyed by uncontrolled overgrowth of the half-starved and miserable populations of the underdeveloped areas, then we are also involved with a long-range threat to our way of life that is just as serious as a war threat, even though it is a more subtle one. The only solution to both short and long-range problems is to end starvation, misery and ignorance as a first step toward achieving a balanced One World, in which some sensible method of placing a ceiling on population growth can eventually be worked out.

If the program is developed under UN auspices, as it should be, the cost should be prorated among all the advanced countries on some equitable basis.

We should approach the immediate problem in terms of how quickly we can accomplish the result desired. In all probability, the more quickly we do the job, the cheaper it will be. The cost to America of perhaps 4 or 5 billion a year for a generation would be a trivial figure compared with the costs of the present cold war. Eventually, much of the cost could probably be repaid, if we finance these projects with long-term low-interest loans. The increased knowledge we will obtain from the experience of conducting such a program will also be a valuable return for our investment.

To win the support of the American people for this program we must have convincing rebuttals for such comments as: "Why should we help them?" "They never did anything for us!" "The more we help them the worse off they are; and we are, too, for our taxes are increased."

Superficially these and many similar comments may contain some truth, but in a deep, historical view, they are dead wrong. We forget that other nations have helped us directly and indirectly in the past, and we are still in their debt. The time has now come for us to pay up. Let us look at the ledger.

First, we are indebted to other nations for the great heritage of knowledge and information in the arts, sciences and humanities; knowledge and information accumulated through the sweat and struggle of the rest of the world and freely shared with us at little or no cost. Second, we owe them for sending us many of the most vigorous, energetic, courageous and talented people who migrated from their countries to ours. Third, many countries, especially France, gave us substantial military assistance during our early history, while we were getting started in business. Regardless of its money cost at that time, this assistance was of great help, and we need now to acknowledge its value. Finally, we should be thankful that many other nations have been the proving ground for experiments in social and political development. We have been able to study their experience and to avoid their mistakes.

We have had a continent-sized storehouse of natural wealth. And for three centuries we had two great oceans providing a protective moat while we exploited that stored natural wealth. We have not only been remarkably lucky in our material and intellectual heritage but we have received valuable direct and indirect assistance from other nations. For all these reasons, we have an obligation to help other people in the world achieve a better way of life. We also have the hard-headed reasons already presented for helping these people which should justify sound Foreign Aid programs. And there is one final question this country must answer as a member of the family of nations: "Am I my brother's keeper?"

Chapter XVI

ONE WORLD OR NONE

It seems beyond doubt that if this country and the U.S.S.R., with their respective allies long continue the present arms race, the end result will be No World. There are two roads to this dead-end—and the expression has never been used more precisely. The obvious way is to blunder or drift into a nightmare nuclear war in which hundreds of millions would be annihilated in a few hours' time, to be followed by millions more who would die of burns, radiation, starvation, pestilence and fallout over the ensuing days, months or years. Such nuclear war might mean the end of man as a living species. It would certainly mean the end of the two ways of life this country and the Soviets each seek to "defend."

The second way to destroy our tenuous world "order," economically, morally and intellectually, is to continue for too long the present cold war, with its costly and wasteful armaments race. There is already evidence of this danger. You don't have to have a degree in economics to realize that the cold war is being carried on at the expense of something else. If the antagonists in the struggle were not spending the equivalent of about 100 billion dollars a year "defending" themselves, they would be spending most of that 100 billion dollars improving the life of their citizens.

It is well to recall that money is merely the symbol of energy. The economic wealth of a country equals the number of working people times the average amount of energy each controls, minus the depreciation cost of replacing the people and machines. Let us convert the 100 billion dollars to units of human work. Let us assume that the annual salary of the average person in all countries working on "defense" is $5,000. By dividing $100 billion by $5,000 we get an approximation of the total number of people engaged in "defense" for the U. S., the U.S.S.R. and their allies. This figure is 20 million. Actually, of course, we are all working at least part-time to support this "defense." So many more than 20 million are involved to some extent. But the 20 million figure is a simpler way to consider the matter.

It is as though, for the past 10 or 12 years, the equivalent of 10

million people have been standing day after day on one side of a
line glaring at 10 million people on the other side. These 20 million
have contributed little if anything to the advancement of civilization. The work they have done, the plans they have made, and
the machines they have accumulated have essentially had to do only
with planning for destruction, not for construction. What makes the
situation worse is that these 20 million people are from advanced
countries and thus are people with advanced "know-how," who could
have made a significant contribution to the world's general progress.
Can humanity afford this? Can America afford this? Are we so
productive that we can continue like this for a generation or two?

The present anemic state of our educational system and the shaky
state of our economy is the price we are paying for our "defense."
The continuing low living standards of the U.S.S.R. and its allies
is the price it is costing them. The turmoil and unrest in the underdeveloped areas of the world are the price those nations are paying.
The inability, under these conditions, to deal with the long-range
population problem is the price that humanity is paying.

If the cold war could be ended, we could put our respective 10
millions to work at constructive projects. We Americans could restore our educational system. And the advanced nations of the
world could, as suggested in the last chapter, give more help to backward nations in developing modern economies. They could begin
to change from their "have-not" status, which is both a short and
long-range menace to the peace of the world. At far less than the
cold war costs, these underdeveloped nations could be brought to
a "have" status of national self-respect and ultimately economic self-
sufficiency.

We saw in an earlier chapter that the over-population of the underdeveloped areas represents a "long range" threat to advanced civilization. The phrase "long range" needs to be defined, because if
the present trend continues unchecked the population of the world
will reach 16 billion in 250 years or less. Historically speaking this
is not long range, it is a very short time in which to solve a social
problem of the magnitude of the population problem. When we
Americans remember how long we have been "solving" the negro
problem in our own country we realize how short 250 years can be.

As already indicated the first stage in any humane and democratic
solution must be to bring these countries as rapidly as possible to
advanced status—so they will possess a literate, educated people.
Only then will these nations be capable of dealing with the population

control problem on a rational basis. If the needed improvements are to be made quickly enough, the advanced countries will have to loan some of their capital to these countries to permit them to industrialize and modernize *more quickly than their national appetite grows.* Unless it is done at such speed they will never be able to accumulate their own reserves of capital with sufficient speed to further accelerate the industrialization and modernization of these areas. It is a grim race between industrialization and overpopulation. The present situation is that population is increasing at an average rate of 3% a year and food producton at perhaps 2½ or 2% or perhaps even less. This is clearly not a formula for progress.

Because of the disparity in rates of social change as compared with industrial change the cities of the world including many U.S. cities are already being filled with displaced, poorly educated, semi-literate, maladjusted, rural "hillbillies"; people who are being displaced from the soil, but who are totally unprepared for industrial city life. Unless some solution is found, far better than anything yet tried, this trend will in the foreseeable future destroy the community life of many American as well as underdeveloped cities, probably before your great grandchildren will be as old as you are.

We achieved the transition from an agricultural to an industrial economy fairly slowly and without too great social difficulty. In 1850, 85% of our people earned their living in agriculture. By 1950 the figure had dropped to 36% and it continues to fall at an ever increasing rate. Our population growth during those years was rapid also but until the past 30 or 40 years we always had cheap land available for excess population to expand into. The shock of temporary population or other economic imbalances could thus be absorbed at our expanding land frontier.

But with the closing of our frontier—that is when *all* the best land had been brought under control, early in this century, we began to have difficulties with excess population or some would say with equitable distribution of industry-earned income. Whichever way you look at it, it's the same coin which simply has two complementary aspects.

But the underdeveloped countries now face a situation in which they have a rate of population growth which surpasses any growth rate the world has ever before witnessed. This population explosion is taking place in predominately agricultural economies in areas of the world which have little if any agricultural land that is not already in use. It is taking place in areas where all kinds of antiquated land use practices place barriers in the way of agricultural efficiency. It is taking place in areas where illiteracy ranges from 50% to 99%, so the possibilities of improving agricultural methods and of introducing industrialization are severely handicapped.

I suggest that as a way out of the present dilemmas of the cold war and overpopulation our country make the following proposal to the United Nations: that a zone of peace be established in the underdeveloped areas; a zone which will exist under a UN *guarantee* that its peaceful status will be maintained. Permission to join the zone of peace would involve two steps. First, any country wishing to join the zone would apply to the UN for permission to do so. The Security Council and General Assembly would need to approve the entry of nations into the zone of peace. This second step which would require Security Council unanimity, would permit the great powers to resolve their conflicting interests before placing any new applicant in the zone. As a further encouragement to underdeveloped nations to join the zone, I suggest we challenge the other advanced nations, and especially the Soviets, to enter into a peaceful competition with us to see how quickly we can bring the underdeveloped countries to an advanced status. By channeling all assistance to these countries through the World Health Organization and UNESCO a mechanism would exist for keeping such "great power" competition from getting out of hand. Nations allowed to join the peace zone would agree to accept developmental assistance only if channeled through UN agencies.

Is such peaceful competition a psychologically sound idea? Is it in harmony with human nature? I think it is because it is based on one factor on which *all* people agree—the desirability of better living. The main trend of man's social evolution, has been toward raising his standard of living, culturally, spiritually and economically. This desire for better living stems from basic human urges and is the *one thing that everyone agrees on!* We should capitalize on this universal desire as the one opportunity for all the advanced countries of both East and West to meet with all the underdeveloped countries of both East and West in a common endeavour.

Is peaceful competition a politically sound idea? When we reach this point in considering this proposal, military-strategic considerations must be taken into account. For, at present, some of the underdeveloped countries possess too great strategic importance to be readily abandoned by one side or other. To meet this problem it would seem that the original zone of peace might consist only of neutral India and perhaps a few similar areas in which neither the U.S. nor U.S.S.R. were strategically involved. Then over the years through a process of negotiation between the "great powers" and other nations desiring to enter the zone of peace the two antagonistic groups would make a series of mutually coordinated strategic withdrawals from other underdeveloped areas. The result would be that at each step we would be enlarging and strengthening the peace zone and at the same time we would be reducing the area of the cold war. Ultimately parts of the advanced areas could even be added and let us hope finally we and the Soviets would ourselves be able to join the ever enlarging zone, thus at last achieving a peaceful One World.

This approach is based on the sound operational principle that when you are confronted with a problem too big to handle, directly, it is wise to finesse it; turn away from the overwhelming aspect and do the little things you can manage. In doing this the bigger problems often grow simpler or at least new approaches become apparent. We have been making precious little progress on the big package—disarmament. Why not try solving a few smaller problems that have some hope of immediate solution?

What specific steps would we need to take if we were to decide to shift from the cold war policy, which accepts a divided world for the indefinite future, to one which begins to look toward a future One World zone of peaceful United Nations? It scarcely needs to be mentioned that such a shift, however desirable theoretically, would only be politically possible if carried out step by step with each side matching the other in concessions at every stage. The Soviets must, of course, match our policy in this respect. I will speak only of what the U.S. plan of action would need to be. The main steps should be these:

1. We would need to accept the idea of competitive co-existence with the Soviets; accept the idea that our differences, however deep, *must* be compromised in some way short of war. This implies biological competition, for it is unthinkable that *all* competition would suddenly stop. As Adlai Stevenson has suggested, we should "invite Mr. Khrushchev to coordinate his [foreign aid] efforts with ours . . .".

We should look on the prospect of peaceful competition in the underdeveloped countries as a heaven-sent opportunity for learning how to live in the same (UN refereed) world with our ideological antagonists. It may be useful to think of this struggle in terms of a bitter quarrel between a husband and wife over an irreconcilable issue—religion for example. The couple may be unable to resolve the central issue, but if they can continue to live together and concentrate on the daily problems of feeding and caring for the children and themselves they may at least keep the religious matter from wrecking their marriage.

Such an approach requires great patience and confidence. The proposal I suggest will require faith that in the long run all people, even the Russians, want a better and a peaceful world. Many who call themselves "realists" will consider such "faith" dangerous. In today's world the only "realists" are the optimists. But until the great powers can somehow develop far greater confidence and trust in each other than is now possible, complete disarmament will be impossible.

It is now quite clear that general disarmament is—in the present state of mutual distrust—utterly unrealistic. I do not mean to imply that *nothing* can be done or that these efforts should stop. But we should add another string to our bow. Peaceful UN refereed competition in biology in a zone of peace could provide an arena for actions comparable to that provided by the International Geophysical Year for obtaining carefully refereed competition whose result will be the gradual enlargement and competitive strengthening of an economically healthy zone of peace. We could thus create an arena in which almost daily small steps toward peaceful understanding could be taken. New and larger ones would follow as we grow in mutual confidence. Through the resulting people-to-people contacts between Americans, Russians and other nationals, sufficient confidence and trust could develop to the point that real "great power" disarmament could ultimately be carried out.

2. We would need to stop considering foreign aid as "welfare," "do-good," or "give-away" programs. No doubt the too-common attitude of antagonism toward these programs is due to the fact that they have been "sold as "do-good" programs. Apparently some of them have also been poorly conceived, and too short-range in concept and too overladen with military goals to have any value more lasting than to increase our tax load. We must minimize such errors, if we want the American tax-payer, who is neither a fool nor a miser, to approve such expenditures. But, as former President Truman has said, "Correct all the mistakes you can . . . improve it . . . eliminate waste and increase efficiency—but don't scuttle the ship just to stop the leaks."

3. There should be no rigid deadlines placed on such projects. Once

the goal is approved, the approach should be— "We'll help you solve the problem—however long it takes." Even a small businessman or independent farmer must project his plans several years in advance, though he still keeps them flexible enough to be modified by new factors. Surely it is absurd to demand short-range and rigid planning on projects of the scale, for example, of the Aswan dam and others of that magnitude, merely in order to meet our antiquated annual budgeting traditions.

Why can't our Congress establish a system of long-term budgeting to meet the realities of modern-sized developments? Incidentally, the deficiencies of short-term budgeting apply to many of our domestic as well as to foreign projects. It should be possible for Congress to establish a system for doing long-term budgeting on a four-year basis, concurrent with each new Presidential term. Annual budgeting would then be done only on short-term items or to make necessary adjustments for unforeseen developments in the long-term projects. Such arrangements could do a great deal to ease the load on Congress and the Administration and strengthen our own political system. It would give the voters an opportunity to express themselves on the overall policies of government in a way not open to them at present.

4. These foreign biological aid programs should, so far as possible, be paid for by the countries being assisted. Of course, they would have to be financed largely with long-term loans. Such loans could only be supplied by direct government loans or by government guarantees of private loans. One way of channeling private money into such long-term loans would be to make them attractive to the general public as an investment for delayed repayment in the retirement years. If individuals could invest in UN 10, 20, or 30-year development bonds, which like our defense bonds would accumulate interest until maturity, and then repay both principle and interest to the individual during his retirement years, it might be possible to raise billions for such purposes. Their security could be guaranteed both by Congress and the World Bank. Since these underdeveloped countries cannot pay a high interest rate something would need to be done to close the gap between the interest charged these governments and what the bonds would need to pay if they are to be sold to private investors. Loans of this type obviously do not fulfill the ordinary banking criteria for good risks. More liberal banking rules need to be adopted and the richer countries and the UN will have to provide a "guarantee" to back up the loans.

5. The objective of these foreign biological efforts should not be to win cold war allies from among these nations, but to create strong and independent peaceful countries. In the words of Vice-President Nixon, these countries should be helped to become economically independent and thereby "politically independent even of the United States."

Because of the ultimately peaceful objective just described we should, in our budgeting, make a clear distinction between foreign aid to improve *their* health, educational and economic well-being, and aid given in order to strengthen *our* defense posture. These two forms of "aid" should be separately identified and separately administered. The public should always be able to distinguish clearly between the two "aids." This step can do much to maintain public support for developmental forms of foreign aid, especially if the military aspects can be gradually deflated through a mechanism such as suggested.

6. We could greatly improve the effectiveness of our technical aid program if we employed the "swarming" principle in our programs for exporting education and technical "know-how." Instead of sending only individual specialists to foreign countries and training only individual foreigners in this country in the hope that they will return to their native lands, we should consider training whole college faculties or whole groups to operate a factory, for example. An American university or college or factory would educate or train people from a foreign country to form the nucleus for a college faculty or a factory or other enterprise. This nucleus augmented by Americans would then "swarm" and establish the institution in the foreign country. Our people would give the new "swarm" support and guidance until it was fully established. The Americans would withdraw when the new institution was functioning, but would maintain cooperative ties to mutual advantage.

"Swarming" would also establish cultural bonds that would further cross-cultural understanding. Of course, in recommending "swarming," I do not advocate putting an end to training individuals. I merely suggest it as an additional approach for areas which need a more concentrated educational or technical "crash program."

A program to export biology in all its forms, as outlined here, may require at least a generation or two. The Marshall Plan, designed for the rehabilitation of the temporarily sick economies of advanced European countries, succeeded in a few years. But in countries as economically backward as many of the underdeveloped nations are it will take much longer to bring them to a level of self-sufficiency. But it is well worth it.

In an earlier chapter we considered how much America has been the beneficiary of technical and scientific "know-how" which we obtained "free" from Europe. We noted that European science was in turn supported by the sweat and toil of billions of African and Asian people working in the colonies of the European nations which then controlled them. If we have any sense of equity, we will now feel a responsibility to repay our debt to humanity through support of the foreign aid program outlined. For those who don't accept this debt argument, there is still the sound personal survival argument already outlined.

The prize of success will be world peace. The penalty for failure may be world death. We have no choice but to accept the challenge. To debate "whether" under these conditions is absurd. The only rewarding questions on foreign aid worth answering at this point are: "What do they need?" "How much?" and "How quickly?"

INDEX